Aerobics and Fitness Association of America

Exercise
Standards & Guidelines
Reference Manual

Group Exercise | Special Populations | Multitraining®

A Reference Manual for Fitness Professionals

Fifth Edition

Published by
Aerobics and Fitness Association of America
1750 E. Northrop Blvd., Suite 200
Chandler, AZ 85286
(800) 466-2322
www.afaa.com
customerservice@afaa.com

AFAA's Mission: AFAA provides comprehensive cognitive and practical education for fitness professionals grounded in research, reflecting a commitment to quality distance education that upholds safe and effective fitness practice.

AFAA and logo, Aerobics and Fitness Association of America, AFP Fitness Practitioner, Fitness Triage, Fitness Gets Personal, Mat Science, American Fitness, FitMarkers, Multitraining Live, Multitraining, and Fitness Management for Life are registered trademarks of the Aerobics and Fitness Association of America. The Sunrise Yoga Format and AFAA 5 Questions are trademarks of the Aerobics and Fitness Association of America. Other marks referenced in this book may be trademarks or registered trademarks of other companies, and are used only for informational purposes and to the owner's benefit, without intent to infringe.

Fifth Edition
Copyright © 2010 by Aerobics and Fitness Association of America
All rights reserved.

First Edition, 1993   Third Edition, 1997
Second Edition, 1995   Fourth Edition, 2002, revised 2005

ISBN 0-9614719-8-0

Printed in the United States of America
10 9 8 7 6

Table of Contents

AFAA's Notice

Part I General Group Exercise

Part II Special Populations

Part III Multitraining®

Part IV References

AFAA's Notice

PLEASE READ BEFORE USING AFAA PROGRAMS AND MATERIALS

The courses and materials offered by the Aerobics and Fitness Association of America (AFAA) are intended to provide general educational information to you in your efforts to educate yourself, obtain relevant professional certification, secure continuing education credits if available to you, and to work with your clients to reach definable goals. "You," as used here, includes, but is not limited to, fitness trainers and other fitness professionals of all kinds, fitness trainer students and other professional fitness students of all kinds, providers of continuing education services, AFAA educational contractors, and all other readers and users of the courses and materials offered by AFAA. The courses and materials of AFAA are intended to provide what is believed to be accurate information. However, please note the following important cautions before making use of AFAA courses and materials.

- To the best of the knowledge of the authors, publishers, and presenters of AFAA courses and materials, the contents of such courses and materials were accurate as of the date of publication and/or presentation. However, you are strongly encouraged to keep yourself informed of new developments in the field to make sure that the contents are still accurate when you consult the courses and materials.
- AFAA courses and materials are made available with the understanding that the authors, publishers, and presenters are not engaged in rendering legal, medical, or other professional services by reason of their authorship, publication, or presentation of such courses and materials. You are strongly encouraged to consult an appropriate legal, medical, or other expert if you are seeking such advice or assistance. This is an especially important precaution in the field of fitness and exercise, personal fitness training, and fitness practice.
- AFAA courses and materials are made available without warranties or guarantees of any kind, express or implied, all of which are disclaimed. By way of example only, and without limiting the general disclaimer given above, the authors, publishers, and presenters of AFAA courses and materials cannot and do not promise or guarantee that the contents of such courses and materials are appropriate for every reader or user, or that use of such courses and materials will result in certification or in obtaining employment, or that, if you are certified, you will be able to obtain third-party insurance payments for any services that you may render to your clients.
- You acknowledge that all of the above-referenced authors, publishers, and presenters are independent contractors whom AFAA has engaged for their respective purposes, and that consistent with their independent contractor status, AFAA neither has nor had any right of control over the manner or methods by which they provide their services, and is not legally responsible for their acts or omissions while performing services in their respective capacities.

- The laws that define the practice of medicine or other health care fields specify that the provision of delineated services are reserved for provision by those who are licensed to provide such services. These laws vary from state to state, and the delivery of service is dependent upon specific circumstances which require independent judgment and decision making. In some states, and under some circumstances, the rendering of services by those who are not so licensed may be actually or potentially in violation of law. For that reason, you are cautioned to obtain specific professional advice about the laws and regulations that may apply to you and your delivery of service in a particular locality.
- The documents, forms, and other content found in AFAA courses and materials are offered as illustrative examples only. No such documents, forms, graphs, or other content should be used or adapted for use in violation of copyright or other applicable law. Since the use of these documents, forms, and other content may have legal implications, you are strongly cautioned to consult a qualified attorney before using or adapting them.
- AFAA courses and materials are not intended to establish or define any specific professional standards that apply to all fitness trainers or other fitness professionals and their clients in all circumstances or to limit the exercise of your independent professional judgment as to what is in the best interest of any particular client. The standard of care that you must observe may change from time to time or vary from place to place, and you are strongly cautioned to familiarize yourself with the standard of care that applies to you.
- All of these cautions apply to you regardless of your location. However, since AFAA courses and materials were prepared for use in the United States, special care should be taken if you are outside the U.S. to make sure you are familiar with the laws and regulations that apply in your country and locality or where services are provided by you.
- Participation in AFAA courses, use of AFAA materials, and/or any certification of a fitness trainer or other fitness professional that may result do not qualify you to approve, endorse, or recommend dietary supplements or other ingestibles, ergogenic aids, or any other products or services that claim to enhance physical performance or appearance, nor does AFAA itself issue any such approvals, endorsements, or recommendations. AFAA disclaims any responsibility or liability for any claim resulting from any such approvals, endorsements, or recommendations that you may offer.
- By participating in and/or using courses and materials offered by AFAA, and as condition for providing and presenting such materials and courses to you, you are acknowledging and agreeing that (a) you are solely responsible for all aspects of the conduct of your business and your practice as a fitness trainer or other fitness professional; (b) you are not sponsored or endorsed by or otherwise affiliated with AFAA by reason of any certification that AFAA may issue to you; (c) AFAA is not responsible or liable in any manner whatsoever for claims or liabilities arising from the conduct of your business; and (d) AFAA disclaims any liability, loss, or damages that may result from the conduct of your business or practice, and/or your use of such courses and materials, and/or the information, advice, and techniques embodied in such courses and materials.

Aerobics and Fitness Association of America

- You acknowledge that you retain sole control over and responsibility for the development and implementation of any course that you develop or engage others to develop for you ("Your Course"), including the responsibility for ensuring that such courses do not infringe or violate the intellectual property rights or contract rights of any third party, and that AFAA's approval of such courses is based strictly on its approval criteria, which cannot and does not consider any such third-party rights. You agree to indemnify and hold harmless AFAA, its owners, shareholders, directors, officers, employees, agents, successors, and assigns from and against any third party claims, demands, liabilities, costs, or expenses, including without limitation reasonable attorney's fees and expenses, resulting from or attributable to any third-party claims that involve or relate to you or your provision of service or your participation in any course.

Part of the foregoing was adapted from a Declaration of Principles of the American Bar Association and a Committee of Publishers and Associations.

Part I

General Group Exercise

Basic Exercise Standards and Guidelines

BASIC EXERCISE
STANDARDS and GUIDELINES

I. Introduction

Introduced in 1983, the Aerobics and Fitness Association of America's (AFAA's) *Basic Exercise Standards and Guidelines* were the first nationally developed standardized guidelines available to fitness professionals to assist them in providing exercise leadership to clients. This revised edition of the guidelines reflects an ongoing process of research, critique, and consensus by a multidisciplinary team of fitness industry experts and organizations. These standards and guidelines apply to adults: (a) without known physiological, biomechanical, or medical conditions that would in any way restrict their exercise activities, and/or (b) adults who have been cleared by their health care provider to exercise. However, the application of these standards and guidelines to the delivery of service is dependent upon the application of individualized professional judgment. It may also be appropriate in the application of independent professional judgment to adapt these guidelines for special populations (e.g., individuals with medical conditions or elite athletes). And, although these *Basic Exercise Standards and Guidelines* emphasize the group exercise setting, many of the principles are applicable for the personal fitness trainer working with individual clients. For more in-depth study, fitness professionals who are also involved in personal training should refer to AFAA's *Personal Fitness Training: Theory & Practice*.

II. General Principles of Exercise Training

A. The FITT Principle: Training Variables

Exercise programs will provide optimal results with minimal risk of injury when developed appropriately. Training variables, such as Frequency, Intensity, Time, and Type, must be considered when designing an exercise program.

- Frequency refers to the number of exercise sessions per week.
- Intensity refers to the difficulty of an exercise or exercise session.
- Time refers to the duration or length of each exercise session.
- Type refers to the mode of activity performed.

It should be recognized that training variables are interrelated and, therefore, each variable may influence the other exercise variables. A significant increase in exercise intensity, for example, will likely result in a decreased duration of that exercise session. Changes in the mode or type of exercise performed may also affect the other training variables. For example, a runner may find that he/she cannot perform the same exercise duration when cycling as when running because the training stresses are applied differently to the body.

B. The Principle of Overload

To achieve desired training improvements or effect, the relevant body system must be overloaded beyond its normal level or present capacities. When the body is stressed in this manner, it then responds by adapting so that its capacity increases. The physiological changes that occur in the body as a result of exercise overload are referred to as a training effect. A training effect will occur if the exercise is sufficient and appropriate in frequency, intensity, and time for a given type of exercise. The principle of overload applies to all types of physical conditioning. Fitness programs that lack overload and/or variation will serve to maintain, but not improve, one's existing level of fitness.

C. The Principle of Progression

For continued improvements in fitness, an exercise program should provide gradual increases or progressions in frequency, intensity, time, and/or type of exercise. Proper progression includes a systematic change in overload over time, designed to maximize fitness gains while keeping the risk of overtraining and related injuries low. For program progressions, allow for the initial conditioning phase to last 4–6 weeks, improvement phase 4–5 months, and maintenance thereafter. Recommended progressions will vary depending on the participant's age, physical limitations, and fitness level.

D. The Principle of Specificity: SAID

Specificity of training is also referred to as the SAID principle: Specific Adaptation to Imposed Demands. The body will adapt to the type of physiological stresses placed on it. In order to improve in a particular area of fitness or sport, the precise movement or movement pattern should be rehearsed. For example, to become a better hurdler, one must jump hurdles. The principle of specificity also applies to the training variables (frequency, intensity, time, and type). For example, to be successful, a marathon runner must include distance running in his/her training program. Cycling would not suffice as his/her main training type. In addition to movement patterns and training variables, the challenge to the physiological systems needs to be specific to the activity performed. For example, the capacities of the aerobic athlete (e.g., runner, cyclist, swimmer) have minimal transference to anaerobic performance (e.g., sprinting, power weight lifting) and vice versa.

E. The Principle of Reversibility

If one's training workload is discontinued or decreased, detraining in performance will occur. Cardiorespiratory fitness generally appears to decrease after only 2 or 3 weeks without training. Muscular fitness (strength and/or endurance) generally appears to decrease after 2–3 months without training.

F. The Principle of Overtraining

The body needs time to recover and the musculoskeletal system needs time to rebuild from the stress of vigorous exercise. When the training variables utilized do not allow sufficient recovery, overtraining of the body can occur. Overtraining can also occur when training volume and/or intensity are too high or too rapidly increased.

III. Health- and Skill-Related Physical Fitness Components

A complete physical fitness program should seek to improve and then maintain each of the common components of health and fitness, used herein to bring about well-being.

A. Health-Related Components

1. Cardiorespiratory Fitness

Cardiorespiratory fitness (aerobic fitness) can be defined as the ability of the body to take in, transport, and utilize oxygen. It involves the capacity of the heart and lungs to exchange and deliver oxygen to working muscles during sustained motion.

2. Muscular Strength and Endurance

Muscular strength is defined as the amount of weight (maximal force) that can be lifted one time by a particular muscle group, whereas muscular endurance is the ability of a muscle group to lift a submaximal (lesser) weight many times. Muscular endurance also refers to the ability of a muscle group to hold (stabilize) a fixed or isometric contraction for an extended period of time.

3. Flexibility

Flexibility (mobility) is commonly defined as muscle suppleness as well as the range of motion available at a joint(s). Adequate mobility also implies that the muscles are able to elongate to accommodate the full range of motion required by the joint(s).

4. Body Composition

Body composition refers to the absolute and relative amounts of the structural components of the body: (a) fat, (b) fluid, (c) muscle/tissue, and (d) bone. Body composition assessments generally focus on body fat since excessive amounts may increase the risk of disease. Maintaining an appropriate level of body fat is essential for good health, and may lower the risk of heart disease, diabetes, and some cancers.

B. Skill-Related Components

Skill-related components of physical fitness may be targeted to achieve improvement in sports, work, or daily life performance as well as help certain individuals avoid serious injury.

1. Agility—ability to change the body's position and direction with quickness and accuracy
2. Balance—ability to maintain equilibrium (or certain posture) while moving or stationary
3. Coordination—ability of the body to utilize the senses and body parts in a harmonious relationship to perform a task smoothly and with accuracy
4. Power—ability or rate at which one can exert strength to perform work quickly
5. Reaction time—the time required to initiate a response to a given stimulus
6. Speed—ability to move the entire body quickly

IV. Health and Fitness Training Recommendations

A. Health Benefits vs. Enhanced Fitness Benefits

In 1996, the *U.S. Surgeon General's Report on Physical Activity and Health* was a call to encourage more Americans to become active. The report states that by becoming moderately active, Americans can lower their risk of premature death and the development of chronic illnesses, such as heart disease, hypertension, and diabetes. Among its major findings were the following points.

- People who are usually inactive can improve their health and well-being by becoming even moderately active on a regular basis.
- Physical activity does not need to be strenuous to achieve health benefits.
- Enhanced fitness or physiological changes occur when the amount (frequency, intensity, and time) of the activity is increased. All American adults should accumulate 30 minutes of moderate physical activity equivalent to brisk walking on most, if not all, days of the week.

In 2008, the U.S. Department of Health and Human Services (USDHHS) introduced the *Physical Activity Guidelines for Americans* which reinforced the 1996 U.S. Surgeon General's Report. The key guidelines for adults are as follows.

1. All adults should avoid inactivity. Some physical activity is better than none, and adults who participate in any amount of physical activity gain some health benefits.

2. For substantial health benefits, adults should perform at least 2 hours and 30 minutes (150 minutes) a week of moderate-intensity (e.g., brisk walking) aerobic physical activity, or 1 hour and 15 minutes (75 minutes) a week of vigorous-intensity (e.g., running) aerobic physical activity, or an equivalent of a combination of moderate- and vigorous-intensity aerobic physical activity. Aerobic activity should be performed in episodes of at least 10 minutes, and preferably, it should be spread throughout the week.

3. For additional and more extensive health benefits, adults should perform 300 minutes (5 hours) a week of moderate-intensity aerobic physical activity, or 150 minutes a week of vigorous-intensity aerobic physical activity, or an equivalent combination of moderate- and vigorous-intensity activity. Additional health benefits are gained by engaging in physical activity beyond this amount.

4. Adults should also perform moderate- or high-intensity muscle-strengthening activities, and involve all major muscle groups on 2 or more days a week since these activities provide additional health benefits.

B. AFAA Fitness Training Recommendations

AFAA supports the guidelines from the American College of Sports Medicine (ACSM) for maximum health and fitness benefits with regard to training recommendations. AFAA also recognizes that the treatment of health conditions, as opposed to the maintenance or enhancement of wellness, should be determined and managed by a licensed health care provider rather than fitness professionals.

AFAA FITT-at-a-Glance

	Cardiorespiratory Fitness	Muscular Strength and Endurance	Flexibility
Intensity/Volume	3–5 days per week * For promoting and maintaining health: 5 days of moderate intensity, or 3 days of vigorous intensity, or a combination of moderate and vigorous intensity 4–5 days per week, along with regular daily activities of living.	Minimum of 2–3 non-consecutive days per week for each major muscle group (arms, shoulders, chest, abdomen, back, hips, and legs); vary exercise selection regularly for maximum results. * Individuals who are new to strength training should begin with 1 set of separate exercises targeting each of the major muscle groups and add additional sets or exercises only after adaptation to the current program has occurred.	Minimum of 2–3 days (ideally 5–7 days) per week for each major muscle and tendon group with special attention to those joints and body segments with a reduced range of motion.
Time	HR_{max}: 64–94% HRR: 40–85% RPE: 6–20 scale: 12–14 (moderate to somewhat hard); 15–16 (hard) or 10-point scale: 4–6 for moderate and 7–8 for vigorous **Volume:** ≥ 1,000 kcal per week (2,000–4,000 may be optimal) • Moderate = 40% to < 60% HRR (or VO_2R) * that noticeably increases HR and breathing • Vigorous = ≥ 60% to 85%HRR (or VO_2R) that results in substantial increases in HR and breathing * Percent VO_2R is determined through clinical laboratory data.	To the point of muscle fatigue while maintaining proper form; typically 8–25 repetitions, 1–4 sets, depending if focus is strength or endurance.	To the end of range of motion, to the point of tightness, without discomfort performing 1–4 repetitions*. * Reference is to statically held stretches.
Frequency	20–60 minutes of continuous or intermittent (10-minute bouts accumulated throughout the day) aerobic activity * For promoting and maintaining health: 30 minutes of moderate intensity or 20–25 minutes of vigorous intensity.	20–60 minutes (time of sessions may vary based on training protocol).	15–60 seconds (per each static stretch). The amount of time spent on flexibility training will be dependent upon the focus and goals of the class. Time may vary from 5–10 minutes to an entire 60-minute class.
Type	An activity that is continuous, rhythmic, and utilizes the large muscle groups (e.g., dancing, walking, hiking, running, jogging, cycling, swimming, stair climbing, inline skating, cross-country skiing, stepping, choreographed cardio kickboxing).	Any activity that creates overload to the musculoskeletal system in the form of external, gravitational, or isometric resistance (e.g., progressive weight training, calisthenics, elastic tubing, stabilization exercises); multi-joint exercises that involve more than one muscle group are recommended to enhance the functional carryover.	Activity that focuses on elongating muscles and moves joints safely through a full range of motion (e.g., yoga, stretch class, cool-down periods).

NOTE: Physical activity (PA) should be preceded by a licensed health care provider examination and clearance for high-risk participants as defined by ACSM and those of moderate risk who wish to participate in vigorous PA. Low-risk participants may pursue a PA program without prior medical exam and those at moderate risk may pursue a moderate-intensity PA program without an exam. Medical clearance should be provided for children, adolescents, or young adults about to enter competitive athletics or vigorous exercise programs.

C. Prevalence of Obesity

It is well established that excessive body fat increases the risks of heart disease, high blood pressure, type 2 diabetes, some forms of cancer, low-back pain, and other musculoskeletal problems. In 2009, approximately two-thirds of American adults were classified as overweight representing a body mass index (BMI) of $\geq$ 25, and about 32% of adults classified as obese (BMI $\geq$ 30). The group exercise setting may lend itself to an educational opportunity regarding body composition and weight management. Class participants can receive their BMI estimations by logging onto http://www.cdc.gov/healthyweight/ assessing/ bmi/.

V. Professional Responsibilities and Concerns

A. Professional Responsibilities

1. Personal Liability Coverage

Since laws vary widely from state to state, it is advisable for instructors to investigate specific legal requirements that are applicable to their particular state. It is recommended that instructors carry comprehensive liability insurance that includes personal injury liability, general liability, and professional liability coverage applicable to their delivery of actual services.

2. Training and Certification

Fitness instructors should complete a training and certification program that incorporates both theoretical knowledge and practical application.

3. CPR/AED and First-Aid Training

Fitness instructors should maintain current nationally and/or internationally recognized adult-level CPR and AED certifications. It is recommended that instructors also receive training in a nationally and/or internationally recognized standard level first-aid course. (For more information, go to www.afaa.com.)

4. Facility Pre-Exercise Participation Screening

A written procedure should be used by the fitness facility regarding pre-participation screening. The Physical Activity Readiness Questionnaire (PAR-Q) is recommended by ACSM as the minimal standard for use by entry-level participants in a moderate-intensity exercise program.

5. Medical Clearance and Pre-Exercise Testing

It is recommended that instructors follow the ACSM guidelines regarding appropriate medical clearance and pre-exercise testing before participation is allowed.

ACSM (2010) revised their recommendations to the following.

- High-risk participants to have a medical exam, medical clearance, and exercise testing before participating in moderate to vigorous exercise. High risk is defined as men and women of any age with one or more of the major cardiovascular, pulmonary, or metabolic disease signs/symptoms or diagnosed with cardiovascular, pulmonary, or metabolic disease.
- Moderate-risk participants to have a medical exam and clearance before participating in vigorous exercise. Moderate risk is defined as men and women with ≥ 2 atherosclerotic cardiovascular disease (CVD) risk factors*, but without symptoms.
- Low-risk participants, in most instances, do not require a medical clearance before participating in moderate to vigorous exercise. Low risk is defined as men and women who are without symptoms and have ≤ 1 CVD risk factor.*

Risk factors include: age, family history, cigarette smoking, hypertension, unhealthy cholesterol levels, prediabetes, obesity, and sedentary lifestyle.

6. **Environmental Monitoring**

   Fitness instructors should check for obvious hazards (e.g., debris, uneven or wet floor surfaces, broken equipment, lighting, room temperature) prior to and throughout an exercise class. When possible, the instructor should try to remedy the hazard. In some cases when hazards cannot be corrected, those hazards need to be reported to management and to participants so they are warned of the hazard. If a warning will not suffice, such as with equipment in need of repair that remains unrepaired, it needs to be removed from service.

7. **Emergency Response Plan**

   All emergencies need to be handled in a professional manner, keeping in mind the best interest of the person needing attention, while ensuring the safety of others. It is recommended that all facilities establish and implement a written emergency response plan. Fitness instructors should have the knowledge to recognize that an emergency exists and to take appropriate action. Such plans should be at least periodically rehearsed and practiced. Some authorities recommend rehearsals at least four times per year. The steps that should be followed in an emergency include the following.

   - Survey the scene.
   - Assess the person in need of attention.
   - Call 911 (or the designated emergency response number).

- Provide appropriate care until emergency medical services (EMS) arrives.

B. Instructional Concerns

1. Exercise Danger Signs

If any one of the following signs are observed or if the participant complains of any of the following symptoms, the participant should stop vigorous exercise immediately and the fitness instructor should assess and implement the need for emergency response procedures.

- Nausea and/or vomiting
- Dizziness, lightheadedness, or unusual fatigue
- Tightness or pain in the chest, neck, arms, jaw, or other bodily areas connoting a potential cardiac problem
- Loss of muscle control, staggering
- Severe breathlessness (gasping) with inability to recover
- Allergic reactions (e.g., rash, hives, anaphylactic shock)
- Blurred vision
- Acute illness
- Mental confusion
- Cyanosis (bluish coloring of skin)
- Acute musculoskeletal injury

2. Signs for Exercise Modification

If any of the following signs are observed or the participant complains of any of the following, he or she should be encouraged to modify or discontinue exercise until the signs disappear. When required, an emergency response plan should be implemented.

- Labored breathing
- Excessive heart rate elevation
- Evidence of strain, holding breath, or unusual redness
- Musculoskeletal pain
- Lack of proper body control

3. Effects of Drugs and/or Medications

Fitness instructors need to be aware that certain prescriptions, as well as nonprescription medications, such as antihistamines and antibiotics, may elicit side effects during exercise similar to those listed under "Exercise Danger Signs" above. Some medications can alter heart rate response (e.g., beta-blockers). Individuals on medications should consult their physicians about possible side effects before beginning an exercise program.

4. **Symptoms of Overtraining**

   Fitness instructors and participants should be aware of the following symptoms of overtraining.
   - Fatigue
   - Anemia
   - Amenorrhea
   - Overuse or stress-related injuries
   - Increased resting heart rate
   - Slower recovery of heart rate
   - Decrease in strength performance
   - Constant muscle or joint soreness on effort or motion, leaning toward pain

5. **Avoiding Overtraining**

   Fitness instructors should recommend (and themselves follow) these suggestions for avoiding overtraining.
   - Vary class type and intensity to alter localized stresses (e.g., step aerobics, low-impact, cycling, pilates, yoga).
   - Limit the number of high-impact or advanced level classes (no more than 8–12 per week and no more than two per day).
   - Always perform an adequate warm-up and cool-down.
   - Limit amount of active demonstration by verbal cueing and use of instructor assistants.
   - Decrease teaching schedule, as needed, when medical conditions or burnout warrant.
   - Ingest a nutritious diet with adequate total calories, carbohydrates, protein, and water.
   - Be aware of, and correct, muscle imbalances.

6. **Hydration and Rehydration**

   Participants should be advised to hydrate before, during, and after exercise, when appropriate based on individual needs, in order to replenish necessary body fluids and to maintain electrolyte balance. Generally, participants should drink approximately 8–12 ounces of fluid shortly before exercise. However, due to the differences in "sweat rates" between individuals and the variation in physical activity, sports, and environmental conditions, it is difficult to assess the actual water and electrolyte losses in a given setting. Therefore, a "one size fits all" recommendation would not be appropriate. In 2007, *ACSM's Position Stand on Exercise and Fluid Replacement* was revised and suggests the following.
   - Participants should monitor their hydration status by taking regular urine and body weight measurements before and after

exercise. Check for color and quantity of urine (should be clear and plentiful).

- Body weight changes can reflect sweat losses during exercise, and can be used to calculate individual fluid replacement needs for specific exercise and environmental conditions. For every pound of weight lost, drink 2 cups of fluid.

Prior to Exercise

- Pre-hydrating with beverages, if determined to be required, should be performed over a period of at least several hours before exercise to allow for fluid absorption and urine output to return toward normal levels.
- Consuming beverages with sodium and/or salted snacks or small meals with beverages can help stimulate thirst and retain needed fluids.

During Exercise

- To prevent hypo-hydration, individuals should develop customized fluid replacement programs that prevent excessive weight loss over the course of the activity (i.e., keeping losses of body weight to <2% from the time of exercise start). The routine measurement of pre- and post-exercise body weights is recommended for determining sweat rates and individualized fluid replacement programs.
- Consuming beverages containing electrolytes and carbohydrates can help maintain fluid-electrolyte balance and exercise performance. Whether to use water or an electrolyte drink to replace vital body fluids is dependent on the type and intensity/duration of the exercise.

After Exercise

- Electrolyte deficits should be replenished. The rate of rehydration should be based on the amount of bodily electrolyte fluid loss. If there is time, consumption of normal meals and beverages is adequate to restore normal water body content.

7. **Attire**

Fitness instructors should wear and recommend appropriate clothing and footwear for the type of activity performed during class. This would include, but is not limited to, the following.

- Fabrics that breathe, rather than those that retain body heat
- Comfortable clothing that doesn't hinder movement
- Shoes with proper design, support, and cushioning

8. **Instructor Etiquette**

   Fitness instructors need to act as role models for their participants, and should always conduct themselves in a courteous and professional manner. Professional work habits include, but are not limited to, the following. Instructors should:
   - arrive on time, fully prepared to teach class;
   - introduce themselves to new class participants;
   - be positive when addressing problem situations;
   - dress neatly and appropriately in a manner that is non-intimidating to participants;
   - communicate with, and/or correct, participants in an appropriate manner, taking care not to offend or embarrass them with either their choice of words, voice tone, "spotting technique," or body language;
   - be sensitive to the needs and requests of the class participants when it comes to music selection, volume, and pitch; and
   - make themselves available for questions before and/or after class.

9. **Class Level**

   When deciding on an appropriate class level (or intensity), many factors should be considered, including class size and differences in participant skill and fitness level. One recommended approach is to teach at an intermediate level, and explain and/or demonstrate to the class how to modify the choreography to achieve both more and less intense variations. However, since beginners tend to follow the instructor's movements, instructors may need to frequently go back and forth between beginner and more advanced versions.

10. **Music Usage, Selection, and Speed**

    AFAA recommends using a music selection that is appropriate to the chosen activity. Different modalities will require different beats per minute (bpm) in order to accommodate each participant's lever length (arms, legs, and torso). It is important to monitor the group to make sure that participants are able to safely complete a full range of motion for the chosen exercises without excessive momentum. If they are unable to perform safely, then instructors need to adjust the tempo/pitch or choose more appropriate music (including ethnic or highly-skilled dance styles).

    Example bpm recommendations include the following.
    - Warm-up: 120–134 bpm
    - Low- and high-impact cardio: 130–155 bpm

- Cardio kickboxing: 125–135 bpm (up to 140 bpm for skilled participants)
- Step aerobics: 118–128 bpm (up to 128–135 bpm for advanced, highly-skilled participants)
- Muscle sculpting: under 130 bpm (unless movements are half-tempo)
- Flexibility training: under 100 bpm

11. Breathing as Applied to the Workout

Breathing should follow a consistent rhythmic pattern throughout exercise. The level of activity will dictate rate and depth of ventilation. In general, inhale and exhale through the nose and mouth in a relaxed fashion. However, some forms of exercise (e.g., yoga) may use different breathing techniques.

- When performing cardiorespiratory movements, breathing can act as an indicator of exercise intensity (e.g., implementing the "talk test"), allowing adjustment of exertion level.
- When performing a strength training movement, exhale during the exertion or hardest phase of the exercise.
- When performing flexibility training movements, breathe calmly, easing into the stretch to help lessen a desire to hold the breath.
- Holding the breath while exercising may induce the Valsalva maneuver (i.e., the glottis closes and creates an unequal pressure in the chest cavity, which may cause a rise in blood pressure).
- Hyperventilating or breathing too hard while exercising can irritate the nasal passages as well as cause lightheadedness.

VI. Exercise Evaluation and the AFAA 5 Questions™

A. Exercise Evaluation

Individuals in a fitness class usually have diverse characteristics and goals. Therefore, more conservative guidelines are recommended than might be otherwise indicated when working one-on-one or with a specialized population, such as elite athletes (e.g., gymnastics, track and field). During exercise evaluation there needs to be a continuum by which instructors in a group setting can evaluate an exercise from two viewpoints—effectiveness (benefits) and potential risk (injury quotient) for the potential participant. With this perspective in mind, AFAA has created the AFAA 5 Questions.

B. AFAA 5 Questions™

1. **What is the purpose of this exercise?**
   Consider: muscular strength or endurance, cardiorespiratory conditioning, flexibility, warm-up or activity preparation, skill development, and stress reduction

2. **Are you doing that effectively?**
   Consider: proper range, speed, or body position against gravity

3. **Does the exercise create any safety concerns?**
   Consider: potential stress areas, environmental concerns, or movement control

4. **Can you maintain proper alignment and form for the duration of the exercise?**
   Consider: form, alignment, or stabilization

5. **For whom is the exercise appropriate or inappropriate?**
   Consider: risk-to-benefit ratio; whether the participant is at a beginner, intermediate, or advanced level of fitness; and any limitations reported by the participant

High Risk   Appropriate Modification

1. Sustained unsupported forward spinal flexion

High Risk   Appropriate Modification

2. Sustained unsupported lateral spinal flexion

3. Repetitive or weighted deep knee bends

4. Bouncy (ballistic) toe touches

High Risk	Appropriate Modification	High Risk	Appropriate Modification

5. Rapid head circles

6. Full plough

7. Full cobra

8. Hurdler's stretch

9. Windmills: a rapid side-to-side movement that combines spinal flexion and rotation

10. Supine double straight leg lifts without spinal stabilization

11. Prone combination double leg/double arm lifts

12. Painful, forced splits

High Risk   Appropriate Modification   **High Risk   Appropriate Modification**

13. Weight-bearing pivots
    on unforgiving surfaces

14. Plyometric moves from
    an elevated surface

The following is a list of some exercises that AFAA does not recommend in a general fitness class due to their high risk-to-benefit ratio on the exercise continuum. Some of the following exercises are commonly performed in other disciplines or practices where they should only be used with proper progression, training, alignment, and supervision. In many cases, these exercises can be modified to lessen their potential risk (areas of stress/ concern are listed in parentheses). It is important to note that these other exercises, done with and without equipment, should not be carried out. Such determinations need to be based upon the application of individual professional judgment.

1. Sustained unsupported forward spinal flexion (spinal ligaments)
2. Sustained unsupported lateral spinal flexion (spinal ligaments)
3. Repetitive or weighted deep knee bends (knee ligaments)
4. Bouncy (ballistic) toe touches (back, hamstrings, and calves)
5. Rapid head circles (cervical spine)
6. Full plough (cervical spine)
7. Full cobra (lumbar spine)
8. Hurdler's stretch (medial knee ligament)
9. Windmills: a rapid side-to-side movement that combines spinal flexion and rotation (lumbar spine)
10. Supine double straight leg lifts without spinal stabilization (lumbar spine)
11. Prone combination double leg/double arm lifts (lumbar spine)
12. Painful, forced splits (ligaments in hip and knee joints, groin area)
13. Weight-bearing pivots on unforgiving surfaces (ankles and knees)
14. Plyometric moves from an elevated surface (compression concerns)

Correct standing
alignment

Incorrect standing
alignment
(posterior pelvic tilt)

Incorrect standing
alignment
(anterior pelvic tilt)

C. Body Alignment

Fitness instructors should monitor participants' body alignment throughout each section of class. There are a number of basic exercise positions to consider, such as standing, lunge, bent-over, seated, supine (lying on your back), prone (lying on your front), side-lying, and kneeling, as well as alignment in movement. The following are key points instructors should keep in mind when evaluating and cueing for exercise body alignment. The standing alignment below has a complete head to toe description. The other positions described will only include specific alignment cues unique to those postures.

1. **Correct standing alignment**
   - Feet are positioned a comfortable distance, about shoulder-width, apart (a little wider for greater stability).
   - Toes point in the same direction as the knees.
   - Legs may be straight or bent, without hyperextending (locking) the knees.
   - Pelvis is neither tipped forward (anterior tilt) nor tucked under (posterior tilt), but is in neutral alignment.
   - Abdominal muscles are engaged (isometrically contracted) and rib cage is lifted.
   - Entire spinal column is in ideal alignment from neck (cervical spine) to pelvis (which means that the four natural curves of the vertebral column are in a balanced relationship to each other; no one curve is excessive).
   - Shoulder blades are slightly down, neither rounded forward nor excessively pulled back.
   - Head should be held high with the ears in line with the shoulders.
   - From a side view, there should be a straight, vertical line from the head to the feet indicating anterior/posterior balance.

2. **Correct alignment for squats (parallel and plié) and lunge (staggered) stances**
   - Toes and knees point in the same direction.
   - Knees do not extend past the toes.
   - Hips are at or above the height of the knees.
   - Hips and shoulders are kept squared to the front.
   - Abdominal muscles are engaged to support the spine in neutral posture.
   - Shoulders are kept down away from ears.

Correct alignment for squats   Correct alignment for lunges

3. **Correct bent-over alignment**
   - The bent-over position may be performed by flexing at the hips or spine.
   - When flexing from the hips, engage the back and abdominal muscles to support the torso in neutral. If additional support is needed, use one or both hands on the thigh(s), floor, or other stable surface (e.g., chair, pole, wall).
   - When flexing from the spine (rounding the back), one or both hands should be placed on the thighs, ankles, floor, or other stable surface or object. The additional support is required because in the forward spinal flexed position, the abdominal and back muscles are not effectively co-contracting to stabilize the torso. Since the spinal extensors are not adequately contracting, there is increased stress to the ligaments and other soft tissue surrounding the vertebrae.

Correct bent-over alignment

4. Correct seated alignment

- Maintain the spine in neutral alignment, with upper body weight directed onto the sitting bones (ischial tuberosities).
- Knees are bent at a 90° angle (if on a chair) or held straight, slightly bent, or folded (if seated on the floor) to facilitate a neutral spine.
- Shoulders are down, scapulae neutral, neck relaxed.
- Toes and knees should point in the same direction to avoid ligament and knee stress.

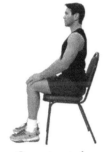   

Correct seated alignment   Correct long seated alignment   Correct straddle seated alignment   Correct cross-legged seated alignment

5. Correct supine alignment

- Lie on back and maintain a neutral spine by engaging the abdominal muscles and placing the pelvis in neutral.
- Some participants will need to keep one or both knees bent with feet flat on the floor in order to maintain a neutral spine.

Correct supine alignment

6. **Correct prone alignment**
   - Lie down with face looking down or turned to one side (head may be placed on forearms).
   - Maintain a neutral pelvis and spine by engaging the back and abdominal muscles.

Correct prone alignment

7. **Correct side-lying alignment**
   - Stack hips and shoulders to maintain a square alignment.
   - Use top arm in a support position by placing the hand on the floor in front of the body.
   - Rest the head on the bottom arm to keep the neck in neutral alignment or support an elevated torso position on the elbow (if in an elevated position, place the elbow directly under the shoulder).
   - If in an elevated position, keep the spine in a straight line rather than allowing the torso to slouch.
   - Knees and hips can be extended or flexed (the flexed position will allow for greater stability).

Correct side-lying alignment

8. **Correct kneeling alignment**
   - Kneeling positions may be performed full-kneeling on two knees with the torso upright or half-kneeling on one knee with the other leg in a 90° forward support position.
   - Kneel on one knee with the other foot in front, placed far enough away that the front knee is bent at no more than a right angle (90°).
   - Remain upright or hinged at the hips (even if one leg is extended), keeping the spine as neutral as possible.
   - Abdominal and back muscles should be engaged.
   - Shoulders should be down with neck in neutral alignment.

Correct full-kneeling alignment   Correct half-kneeling alignment

9. **Correct hands (or elbows) and knees alignment**
   - Place the hands or elbows on the floor directly under the shoulders.
   - Kneel with knees directly under the hips.
   - Keep shoulders and hips square.
   - Keep the neck in neutral alignment.
   - Engage the abdominal muscles to maintain neutral spinal alignment (avoid arching the low back).

Correct hands and knees alignment   Correct elbows and knees alignment

10. **Correct alignment while moving**
   - Maintain all of the above mentioned points as they apply to the execution of an exercise or the body in movement.
   - Alignment will vary according to the specific requirements of the desired exercise or movement.
   - Participants should control their range of motion in order to maintain posture and alignment throughout all movements.

Correct alignment
while moving

VII. Group Exercise Class Format

The format/design of a class should reflect sound application of the principles of training so that fitness gains are fostered while injury risks are kept at a minimum. Depending upon the class type and objectives, the format will vary. However, AFAA does recommend that every class include the following components.

- Pre-class announcements
- A warm-up/activity preparation period
- Body of the workout (e.g., cardio, strength, flexibility training)
- Post-exercise relaxation, stretching, and/or cool-down

VIII. Class Components

A. Pre-Class Announcements

The fitness instructor should introduce himself or herself and announce the type, level, and format of the class. He/she should ask if there are any new participants and remind them to work at their own level. Let participants know what type of intensity monitoring will be utilized and be sure they are familiar with it.

B. Warm-Up

1. **Definition, Purpose, and Duration**

Definition

A warm-up is the preparation period for a specific workout.

Purpose

The warm-up should increase core temperature as well as prepare the muscles and joints for movements that will follow. This can be accomplished by combining limbering and movement rehearsal, and/or light preparatory stretches when appropriate. A proper warm-up should prepare the body for vigorous exercise and may reduce the risk of injury.

Duration

The duration of the warm-up will be dependent on the length and type of class, as well as fitness level and age of the participant. A typical warm-up period for a group exercise class is 8–12 minutes. However, it may vary (e.g., 5–10 minutes) depending on the type of exercise and class design. Keep in mind that in a cardio workout, there may not be a clear-cut demarcation between the warm-up and cardio sections.

2. **Common Warm-Up Methods**

Movement Rehearsal

Movement rehearsal involves performing lighter or less intense versions of movements or patterns that will be used in the workout to follow (e.g., low kicks prior to a vigorous kickboxing segment, marching prior to higher impact jogging, or performing resistive movements without weights prior to the weighted segment). The goal is to increase the blood flow and core temperature as well as facilitate performance and coordination.

Limbering Movements

Limbering movements are smooth, moderately-paced, non-weighted, full-range movements that increase joint mobility and core temperature (sometimes referred to as "dynamic stretching"). Examples would include shoulder circles, overhead arm reaches, side-to-side lunges, and other fluid movements. In some cases, there will be a similarity between limbering and movement rehearsal.

Preparatory Stretching

Preparatory stretches are gentle stretches (held for less than 15 seconds, typically 8–16 beats of music). These stretches are designed to ease the muscles through a range of motion to ensure proper movement mechanics rather than increase isolated muscle flexibility. Over the years, controversy has arisen within the fitness industry regarding whether or not to include stretching within the warm-up. Until further research is compiled, AFAA's stance is that light, preparatory stretching is optional based on the needs of the participants, activity, or environment, while more intense or longer-held stretches (> 15 seconds) should not be included as part of a warm-up, but rather during the post-workout flexibility section.

NOTE: AFAA recommends the use of an appropriate combination of the above mentioned methods, taking into consideration those muscles that are commonly tight and need special attention for the intended workout, fitness level of participants, time of day, environmental temperature, and so forth.

3. Special Considerations

Intensity and Impact

It is important to keep the participants below their training heart rate range during a warm-up. Movements should be low intensity and build gradually. Movements or repetitions that lead to muscle fatigue are inappropriate. High-impact movements that travel laterally should be avoided until the ankles and feet are sufficiently warmed up (usually 3–4 minutes).

Speed and Control

Movements and stretches performed too rapidly or without control can become ballistic (bouncy or jerky with momentum). This type of movement may induce the stretch reflex (i.e., muscle contracts against the stretch in a protective manner) and may increase the risk of injury. Therefore, it should be avoided.

Range of Motion (ROM)

When beginning a warm-up, start with moderate ROM move-ments and slowly build to a greater ROM as the body warms up. Although some participants may be flexible enough to omit statically-held stretches, instructors should keep in mind that others in a group may benefit from gentle static stretching.

Sequence

Follow any order, making sure to include all major muscle groups. Warming up from either head to toes, or vice versa, is an easy way to avoid omitting any muscle groups.

Spinal Issues

Make sure to prepare the spine with controlled movements in all functional ranges (including flexion, extension, rotation, and lateral flexion). Participants who have a history of low-back in-juries should perform the single-plane movements of back flex-ion and extension prior to rotation and/or lateral flexion of the spine. Avoid sustained, unsupported forward or laterally flexed positions of the spine (rounding the back or side bending), as over stretching of the ligaments in the lower back may occur. Support the torso by placing hands on the thighs, depending upon individual flexibility level.

4. **Sample Exercises**

   Common warm-up movements for the upper body
   - Movement Rehearsal or Limbering: alternating rear shoulder circles, non-weighted front and rear flys
   - Optional Preparatory Stretches: chest and anterior deltoid stretch

   Common warm-up movements for the middle body
   - Movement Rehearsal or Limbering: overhead reaches, light-range alternating punches
   - Optional Preparatory Stretches: supported spinal forward and lateral flexion

   Common warm-up movements for the lower body
   - Movement Rehearsal or Limbering: marching in place, step touch, knee lifts
   - Optional Preparatory Stretches: standing calf, standing hip flexor

Sample Warm-Up Movements

Movement Rehearsal and Limbering

Preparatory Stretches

C. Cardiorespiratory Training

1. Definition, Purpose, and Duration

Definition

The cardiorespiratory section of class utilizes continuous and rhythmical aerobic activities that target the large muscles of the body to create an increased demand for oxygen over an extended period of time. Modalities include, but are not limited to, walking, hiking, stepping, high/low-impact aerobics, stationary cycling, inline skating, and cardio kickboxing.

Purpose

Cardiorespiratory training exercises improve the heart, circulatory, and pulmonary systems. This can be accomplished by utilizing a variety of training methods that target cardiorespiratory endurance (e.g., continuous, interval, and circuit training).

Duration

The duration will vary depending on the class format and level, but will typically last 20–45 minutes in a 60-minute class (or several short bouts of 10 minutes each in a circuit format).

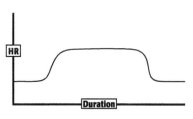

Bell Curve Graph (Steady State)

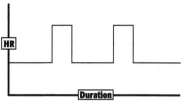

Interval Training Graph

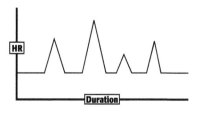

Intermittent Training Graph

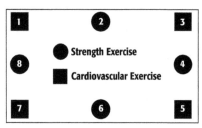

Circuit Training Diagram

2. Methods of Cardiorespiratory Training

Continuous or Steady-State Training

Cardio exercises are performed in such a way that the intensity gradually increases, is held at steady state for the majority of the workout, and then gradually decreases. Choreography is developed in such a way that intensity fluctuations are minimized in an attempt to keep the heart rate at a certain level within the training (target) heart rate range (THRR). If plotted on paper, the intensity of continuous steady state training would depict a flat top bell curve.

Interval Training

Interval training is characterized by timed bouts of higher-intensity work followed by periods of lower-intensity active recovery. During the work phase, participants perform movements that may take them to anaerobic levels (above their aerobic THRR), or to the high end of their aerobic range. During the active recovery, participants work at or below the low end of their aerobic THRR. The work and recovery phases are performed in a timed ratio. For example, 1:3 (30 seconds of work followed by a 90-second recovery).

Intermittent Training

This training method is also known as variable intensity training or spontaneous training. It is a less structured form of interval training with randomly interspersed peak movements followed by lower-intensity movements.

Circuit Training

Circuit training involves timed bouts of activities/exercises performed in a station-to-station, or sequential, manner. A class can perform a circuit in a stationary position with all participants performing the same activity simultaneously, or with participants moving around the room from station to station performing different exercises. These activities can be designed to improve cardiorespiratory endurance, muscular strength, or a combination of both. A greater cardiorespiratory benefit will occur if all the activities or stations are cardiorespiratory in nature.

NOTE: AFAA recommends the use of any or all of the aforementioned cardiorespiratory training techniques. If higher-intensity interval training is used, participants should be advised to limit or space workout times to allow for adequate recovery.

3. Special Considerations

Monitoring Intensity

10–15 minutes during the activity, as well as at the completion of the post-aerobic cool-down. A variety of methods, such as pulse check, rating of perceived exertion, talk test, or a heart rate monitoring device, can be used effectively as long as proper monitoring techniques have been taught.

Heart rate
wrap around method

Heart rate
finger tip method

Cross-Training

Participants and fitness instructors should cross-train by varying the modalities of their cardiorespiratory activities to help decrease biomechanical stress, avoid mental burnout, and increase adherence.

Intensity Issues

Instructors should offer a variety of intensity options/modifications for movements to allow participants to stay within their proper training range. Commonly used options include the following.

- Adding or eliminating dynamic arm movements
- Adding or eliminating impact or propulsion
- Increasing or decreasing the range of a movement
- Increasing or decreasing the speed of a movement
- Making a pattern of movements that may be either more or less intricate
- Substituting moves (e.g., marching rather than jogging)

It is recommended that individuals who are moderately to highly deconditioned start with intensities that are slightly lower (e.g., 64–74% of HR_{max} or 40–55% of HRR/VO_2R), remain in a comfort zone (around "moderate" on RPE scale), and gradually increase over time.

Music Speed

If using music with choreography, AFAA recommends music speeds that will allow the arms and legs to move throughout their full range of motion with control while maintaining proper form and alignment. (See section V.B.10.)

Range of Motion

Participants should control their range of motion in order to maintain posture and alignment throughout all movements. The movement in the limbs needs to match the ability to stabilize the core of the body (e.g., avoid kicking so high that the back cannot remain upright, but flexes to compensate). When performing certain moves, participants must be sure to complete a full range of motion (e.g., when performing impact moves, with the exception of lunges or repeating lunges, bring the heels to the floor on each landing).

Repetitive Stress Issues

To help prevent repetitive stress injuries, avoid extended periods of consecutive movements, such as hops, kicks, jumps, or punches. For example, use a variety of high-, low-, and mid-range elevation of the arms to avoid stressing the shoulders and avoid hopping on one leg for more than eight consecutive counts.

Cardiorespiratory Cool-Down (Post-Aerobic)

At the end of the cardiorespiratory segment, AFAA recommends performing 3–5 minutes of lower-intensity rhythmic activity. An appropriately designed cool-down will help participants avoid blood pooling in the extremities as well as aid them in a gradual heart rate recovery. Fitness instructors may also want to include some upright static stretches to regain the range of motion and flexibility in muscles that have been shortened during the workout.

4. Sample Cardio Movements

D. Muscular Strength and Endurance Training

1. Definition, Purpose, and Duration

Definition

Muscular strength and endurance training involves working individual or groups of muscles against a resistance to the point of muscle fatigue. Different forms of resistance can be used, such as dumbbells, weighted bars and balls, resistance tubes, or body weight. Example workouts include calisthenics/floor work, body sculpting, or circuit training.

Purpose

Both muscular strength and muscular endurance are important for overall health. Benefits include an improved ability to perform everyday activities, increased muscle mass, increased metabolism, stronger bones, decreased risk of injury, improved posture and symmetry, and improved athletic performance.

Duration

The time required for muscular training varies depending on the type and format of the class. A typical strength workout lasts between 45 and 60 minutes, including the warm-up and flexibility work. If the strength training is only a portion of the workout, it may only last 15–20 minutes. In the latter case, fewer muscle groups may be targeted (e.g., upper body and abdominals only).

2. **Common Methods of Muscular Strength and Endurance Training**

    In a group exercise setting, exercises will involve either concentric, eccentric, or isometric muscular contractions.

    - Concentric Muscular Contraction: A concentric contraction occurs when tension generated by the muscle is sufficient to overcome a resistance and moves (at a joint) a body segment of one attachment toward the segment of its other attachment (e.g., the upward or shortening phase of a biceps curl).
    - Eccentric Muscular Contraction: An eccentric contraction occurs when a muscle slowly lowers a resistance (lengthening phase) as it returns from its shortened phase to normal resting length.
    - Isometric Muscular Contraction: An isometric contraction describes a static (held) position in which tension is developed in the muscle, but the muscle length and joint angle do not change.

    NOTE: The following methods and exercises use one or both types of muscle contraction(s).

    Muscle Isolation (Prime Movement)

    Isolation exercises are used to target a specific muscle group by utilizing the primary movement (joint action) of that particular muscle. Examples include biceps curls, calf raises, and deltoid raises.

    Multi-Joint/Multi-Muscle

    As the name implies, multi-joint exercises involve more than one joint and target several muscle groups in the same exercise. In a squat, for example, movement occurs at several joints (hip, knee, and ankle) and many muscles (quadriceps, gluteal muscles, and hamstrings) are targeted simultaneously.

    Torso Stabilization

    Commonly referred to as torso, core, or spinal stabilization, these exercises will enhance the ability to maintain proper spinal alignment and posture. The primary focus of these exercises is to keep the axial skeleton (torso) stable, whether in a held position against gravity (e.g., modified V-sit) or resisting the movement of an extremity (e.g., supine alternating toe taps, with low back held in neutral). To be executed correctly, the abdominal and back muscles must work together in a co-contracting isometric manner.

Functional Training

Functional training describes exercises that replicate movements commonly used in activities of daily living. A narrow stance squat, for example, duplicates the action of getting in and out of a chair. In many cases (e.g., the squat), functional exercises are not always separate or distinct from multi-muscle /multi-joint or stabilization exercises.

NOTE: AFAA recommends that a combination of the aforementioned training techniques be used in most fitness programs. Each technique challenges the body differently and offers distinct training benefits. The key to exercise selection is based on the participants' goals, their ability to maintain proper form and alignment, and the amount of available training time.

3. **Special Considerations**

Muscle Balance

Muscle balance is achieved when muscles on all sides of a joint are properly trained for proper posture, body mechanics, and injury prevention. Thus, for every primary muscle worked (agonist), the opposing muscle group (antagonist) should also be worked. It is important to note that although both agonist and antagonist muscles should be trained, not all muscles have the equal capacity of their opposers (e.g., calves and anterior tibialis).

It is important for the instructor to be familiar with the most common muscle imbalances so that class time is used wisely. In general, weak, loose muscles (thoracic and upper back) need to be strengthened or tightened, and excessively tight muscles (chest and anterior deltoids) need to be stretched or lengthened.

Range of Motion

Isotonic exercises should be taken through a full ROM. This will allow the muscle to function at its best throughout its usable range, as well as to maintain adequate joint mobility. Care should be taken not to overload a muscle past its ability to control the movement. Control is often compromised when working at either end of the range of motion—the beginning and end of the motion are often weaker than mid-range.

Speed and Control

Muscle conditioning exercises should be performed at slow-to-moderate speeds that allow full range of motion and concentrated work in proper alignment. Performing an exercise too quickly often relies on momentum; this is both less effective and more likely to lead to joint or muscle injury.

Intensity

Train a muscle or muscle group to the point of muscle fatigue. Adjust the resistance so that the muscle is fatigued within a reasonable number of repetitions (generally 8 to 15). In group exercise, adjustments of training variables, such as the number of repetitions (up to 25), sets (1–4), or sequencing, may be necessary if the equipment does not offer sufficient resistance.

Torso Stabilization Exercises

If inadequate abdominal strength is present, certain torso stabilization exercises may place inappropriate stress on the spine. In a group exercise setting, extreme care should be used and sufficient modifications properly cued to accommodate individual needs with these torso stabilizing exercises. Properly performed stabilization exercises can be a positive complement to traditional isotonic forms of abdominal training (e.g., crunches and curls). Both methods may be included in a complete training program.

Resistance Equipment Techniques

Participants should not use external resistance (e.g., weights or resistance tubing) until they can perform the given exercises with proper alignment and technique without resistance. When all the repetitions can be completed comfortably with proper form, the amount of resistance should be gradually increased in order to continue to overload the muscles and stimulate improvement. Some general points to keep in mind when cueing exercises that use resistance equipment are as follows.

- Keep the hands relatively relaxed. Avoid a tightly clenched fist; this can potentially cause blood pressure elevation.
- Maintain a neutral wrist. Avoid flexing or extending the wrists while gripping weights, bands, or tubes. Excessive repetitive wrist flexion or extension can increase the risk of carpal tunnel syndrome and tennis elbow.
- Teach participants to bend over and pick up their equipment properly for low-back pain prevention. One hand is on the thigh for support, while the other hand picks up the weight or tubing. For picking up heavier items, use correct squatting technique and a two-handed lift.
- For exercises that are not equipment based, position the muscle so that it is directly opposed by gravity for the most effective and time-efficient work.

- When using elastic resistance, it is important to control the eccentric, or return, phase of the exercise; "rebounding," or suddenly returning to the starting position without control, can cause injury. Additionally, for healthy joint mechanics, the instructor needs to be attentive to utilizing tubing only when there is correct line of pull.

Muscle Conditioning Exercises in the Water

Water exercise differs from land exercise in several important ways. Instead of gravity constantly exerting a downward force (as on land), there is the upward force of buoyancy in the water. In addition, muscle actions are different; all actions in the water are concentric (shortening), whereas on land the actions are both concentric and eccentric (lengthening). Because of these differences, instructors may need additional training or experience in working in water.

4. **Sample Exercises**

The following chart is a compilation of a variety of common exercises. The exercises listed are organized into several approaches to exercise selection. It may also be used as a reference chart to primary muscles and their joint actions.

Table 1.1.

Body Part/ Muscle	Prime Movement (joint action that isolates targeted muscle)	Exercise Variations are Based on Body Position (appropriate in a group exercise class with gravity, weights, or tubing for resistance)	Exercises Single-joint	Exercises Multi-joint	Exercises Stabilization
Shoulders/ deltoids	Shoulder flexion, extension, abduction, horizontal abduction	**Standing:** Raises, upright rows, overhead presses **Seated:** High rows with elastic tubing, overhead presses **Prone:** Push-ups **Supine:** Dips **Bent over:** Posterior raises	Anterior, lateral and posterior raises, rotation	Push-ups and upright rows	Planks, hovers (down position of push-up)
Front of upper arm/ biceps	Elbow flexion	**Standing:** Variety of curls **Seated:** Lat pull-downs and seated rows, variety of curls and rows	Curls	Pull-ups and rows	Bent arm hangs
Back of upper arm/ triceps	Elbow extension	**Standing:** Wall push-ups, overhead extensions **Seated:** Dips, overhead extensions **Prone:** Push-ups **Supine:** Presses **Bent over:** Kickbacks	Kickbacks	Dips, push-ups, presses	Planks
Muscles of the lower arm/a variety of small flexor and extensor groups	Wrist and finger flexion, extension, forearm supination and pronation, wrist abduction and adduction	**Standing and Seated:** Variety of flexion and extension exercises	Wrist curls and extensions, wrist abduction and adduction	Rotation curls	Weight-bearing or weight-holding positions with wrist in neutral alignment
Chest/pectorals	Horizontal shoulder flexion/adduction, and medial rotation of the arm	**Prone:** Push-ups **Supine:** Flys, chest presses, pull-overs	Flys	Bench presses, push-ups	Basic planks and hovers
Upper mid-back: trapezius and rhomboids	Scapular elevation, adduction/retraction	**Standing:** Shrugs, upright rows **Seated:** Rows (with tube), overhead presses **Prone:** Reverse flys **Bent over:** Rows and reverse flys	Straight arm scapular retraction	Rows and overhead presses	Reverse planks
Mid-back: latissimus dorsi	Shoulder joint adduction and extension	**Standing:** Pull-downs (with tube) **Seated:** Pull-downs and rows (with tube) **Supine:** Pull-overs **Bent over:** Rows		Rows and pull-ups	Bent arm hangs and side planks

Body Part/ Muscle	Prime Movement (joint action that isolates targeted muscle)	Exercise Variations are Based on Body Position (appropriate in a group exercise class with gravity, weights, or tubing for resistance)	Exercises Single-joint	Exercises Multi-joint	Exercises Stabilization
Anterior torso/ rectus abdominis, obliques	Spinal flexion, lateral flexion and rotation	**Seated:** V-sits **Supine:** Curls (all variations) **Hands and knees:** Pelvic tilts **Side-lying:** Lateral flexion		Curls, reverse curls, rotation curls	V-sits, supine leg presses, basic planks, and hovers, exercises performed in non-supported hip flexion
Posterior torso/ erector spinae	Spinal extension	**Seated:** V-sits **Prone:** Leg and arm lifts **Hands and knees:** Opposite arm and leg lifts		Prone or on hands and knees: opposite arm and leg lifts	V-sits, reverse planks, exercises performed in non-supported hip flexion
Buttocks/glutei	Hip extension and external rotation	**Standing:** Rear leg lifts, lunges and squats **Prone:** Rear leg lifts **Supine:** Hip lifts **Hands and knees:** Rear leg lifts	Rear leg lifts	Lunges and squats	Standing balance work, reverse planks
Anterior thigh/ iliopsoas, quadriceps	Hip flexion and knee extension	**Standing:** Front leg or knee lifts, lunges and squats **Seated:** Knee extensions and single straight leg raises **Supine:** Knee extensions and single straight leg lifts	Knee extensions, single straight leg raises	Lunges and squats	Standing balance work, wall sits
Posterior thigh/ hamstrings	Knee flexion and hip extension	**Standing:** Hamstring curls, lunges and squats **Prone:** Rear leg lifts and hamstring curls **Supine:** Hip lifts **Hands and knees:** Rear leg lifts and hamstring curls	Hamstring curls and rear leg lifts	Lunges and squats	Standing balance work, reverse planks
Outer thigh/ gluteus medius and tensor fasciae latae	Hip abduction	**Standing:** Abduction leg lifts, single leg squats **Supine:** Hip abduction **Side-lying:** Abduction leg lifts	Abduction side leg lifts		Single leg squats, single leg balance work, side planks
Inner thigh/ hip adductors	Hip adduction	**Standing:** Adduction leg lifts, single leg squats **Supine:** Hip abduction **Side-lying:** Adduction leg lifts	Adduction leg lifts	Plié squats with drag	Single leg squats, single leg balance work
Anterior lower leg/tibialis	Dorsi flexion	**Standing:** Toe raises **Seated:** Ankle flexion	Toe raises		Walking on heels
Posterior lower leg/ gastrocnemius, soleus	Plantar flexion	**Standing:** Heel raises **Seated:** Plantar flexion (with tubing)	Heel raises	Jumps	Walking or balance work on toes

Sample Muscular Strength and Endurance Exercises

wrist curls

rows

triceps dip

back extensions

hover

reverse plank

side plank

abdominal curl with rotation

abdominal curl–straight

V-sit

rear leg lift

toe raises

knee extensions

bent knee hip extension   leg adduction   leg abduction   lateral raises   heel raises

E. Flexibility Training

1. Definition, Purpose, and Duration

Definition

Flexibility training focuses on joint mobility and muscle suppleness, muscle flexibility, and the reduction of muscular tension. When performed as a segment of a class, it usually takes place in conjunction with a post-aerobic cool-down, or the final relaxation segment. Some common flexibility-based classes include fitness stretching and yoga. Some classes, such as yoga, promote a blend or combination of muscular strength and flexibility.

Purpose

Flexibility training improves joint mobility. Having adequate and balanced flexibility may decrease the risk of potential injury and may enhance physical performance.

Duration

The amount of time spent focusing on flexibility training will be dependent upon the focus and goals of the class. The time allotment may vary from as few as 5–10 minutes (near the end of a cardiorespiratory training session) to an entire 60-minute stretching class.

2. Common Methods of Stretching

Static Stretches

Static stretching involves placing the targeted muscle or muscles in a position of elongation and holding that position. Individuals are recommended to perform 1–4 repetitions for each stretch holding for 15–60 seconds. In a group exercise setting 1 repetition may be appropriate, due to time allocation, to target all the major muscle and tendon groups.

Dynamic Stretching/Full Range of Motion

Dynamic stretching involves stretching with movement through a full range of motion. These stretches can range in intensity from a controlled, limbering movement to a ballistic, forceful one. For the purposes of group exercise, the focus should be on multiple repetitions of a controlled movement, ideally contracting the antagonistic muscle while slowly moving through the end range of motion.

Proprioceptive Neuromuscular Facilitation (PNF) Stretches

PNF stretches involve an active contraction of the muscle prior to the stretch (often referred to as the contract/release method). PNF stretching has been shown to be as effective or more effective than static stretching. To properly perform most PNF stretches, outside assistance is needed. Some stretches can be achieved with the use of a towel or stretching strap, but in most cases a trained assistant or physical therapist is needed. For this reason, PNF stretching is not often used in the group exercise environment.

3. **Special Considerations**

Intensity

Stretch to the end of the range of motion or to the point of tension. Never stretch past the point of discomfort or to the point of pain, which may result in microscopic tears in the stretching muscle.

Speed and Control

Dynamic stretches, when performed too forcefully or quickly, become ballistic. This type of movement may induce the stretch reflex mechanism that shortens rather than lengthens the muscle to be stretched. In addition, ballistic stretches increase the risk of injury and should be avoided for the general fitness population. However, ballistic stretching may be more appropriate for individuals who are participating in sports involving ballistic movements.

Range of Motion

Stretch a muscle through its available range of motion. Stretching beyond the muscle's current range of motion can result in injury to the connective tissue and supporting structures.

Body Temperature

Ideally, there should be a noticeable increase in muscle or body core temperature, whether induced by previously performed exercises or external factors (e.g., clothing or room temperature), prior to performing flexibility work.

4. **Sample Exercises**

Common Upper Body Stretches
- Pectorals/Anterior Deltoids
  Level I: Standing—hands behind head
  Level II: Seated—hands behind back
- Upper Back/Mid-Trapezius/Rhomboids/Posterior Deltoids
  Level I: Standing—upper back stretch
  Level II: Seated—hug knees
- Triceps
  Level I: Standing—support hand is in front of body
  Level II: Seated—hand behind head
- Neck
  Level I: Standing—ear to shoulder
  Level II: Seated—ear to shoulder, opposite arm extended down

Common Middle Body Stretches
- Low Back
  Level I: Standing—spinal flexion with hands supporting
  Level II: All-fours position—cat stretch
- Latissimus Dorsi
  Level I: Standing—one arm overhead
  Level II: Kneeling—extended seal
- Obliques
  Level I: Standing—single arm overhead reach
  Level II: Supine—spinal rotation
- Rectus Abdominis
  Level I: Standing—both arms overhead reach
  Level II: Prone—modified cobra

Common Lower Body Stretches
- Hamstrings
  Level I: Standing—single leg sit back
  Level II: Supine—single leg lift
- Quadriceps
  Level I: Standing—modified lunge
  Level II: Standing—bent knee hand holds foot
- Hip Abductors
  Level I: Standing—leg crosses behind
  Level II: Seated—bent knee cross
- Hip Adductors
  Level I: Standing—side lunge
  Level II: Seated—bent knee butterfly

Sample Flexibility Exercises

chest stretch

kneeling reach

supine spinal stretch

cat/back stretch

lateral torso stretch

spinal twist

abdominal stretch

seated adduction and
back stretch

supine hamstring stretch

seated hamstring stretch

supine gluteal stretch

seated gluteal stretch

standing hip flexor and
quadriceps stretch

kneeling hip flexor and
quadriceps stretch

neck stretch

supine twist

F. Final Class Segment

1. Definition, Purpose, and Duration

Definition

The final class segment is the closure of a workout, in which instructors can include stretching and/or other relaxation and stress reducing techniques.

Purpose

The final class segment is designed to promote mind-body awareness and facilitate the relaxation response, a state in which the heart rate and blood pressure are decreased, muscles relax, and physiological stress is reduced. It is an optimal time for participant education. It also provides a sense of completion.

Duration

The time allotment for the final segment of the class will vary depending on the instructor's class design, typically 5–10 minutes.

2. Common Relaxation Methods

Physical Focus

This method focuses on the participants' bodily systems and sensations in an attempt to increase relaxation. This can be done through a variety of methods using careful verbal cueing and/or calm, peaceful music.

Mental/Abstract Focus

This method uses the participants' imagination in order to create a greater sense of relaxation.

Combination Focus

It is common for instructors to combine both the physical and mental focuses in order to see even greater relaxation responses than either method might produce on its own.

3. Special Considerations

Heart Rate Monitoring

It is a good idea to take a post-exercise heart rate or exertion check at the end of class. Participants should notice that their heart rates have returned back, or near, to their pre-exercise heart rates. This final heart rate can help participants increase their appreciation of relaxation for stress management.

Saunas and Hot Tubs

Saunas, hot tubs, steam rooms, and the like are problematic for some individuals if they have not sufficiently cooled down after exercising and for others with adverse health conditions. If core temperature is still elevated post-exercise, taking the body into a hot environment can increase the risk of a heat-related disorder. Heart rate can be an indicator of increased internal temperature and potential heat stress, especially if the post-exercise heart rate is greater than 110 bpm.

Method Selection

When choosing an appropriate final class segment method, be sensitive to language that might make participants uncomfortable. For example, some attendees aren't comfortable with spiritual comments or affirmations in the exercise setting.

4. **Sample Exercises**

Breathing (Physical Focus)

Diaphragmatic breathing is used to decrease stress and tension, and to enhance the relaxation response. In a proper diaphragmatic breath, cue participants to lower the diaphragm on the inhale, causing air to flow into the lungs. The deeper the inhale, the more the diaphragm drops, causing the abdominals to be displaced outward—the abdomen relaxes out. On the exhale, cue them to allow air to flow up and out of the lungs, the diaphragm rises, and the abdominals relax back in. This type of breathing is physiologically correct, usually very relaxing, and is a valuable stress reduction technique. This is the most basic breathing technique used by fitness instructors, although there are many other choices.

Breathing (Combined Focus)

"Lie on your back in a comfortable position, legs relaxed and slightly apart, arms a little distance away from the body, palms facing the ceiling, eyes closed. Allow your abdomen to rise and fall as you slowly and rhythmically breathe. Think of filling a balloon all the way to the bottom with each breath. Let each breath become slower and slower, taking the deepest, most relaxing breaths of your day. Imagine that fresh, healing oxygen is rushing in to nourish every cell on each inhale. Imagine that stale, tired air is carrying out unnecessary tension on each exhale."

The Contract and Relax Method (Physical Focus)

This method is also known as the progressive relaxation technique. It is used to help increase body awareness and release muscular tension. Cue participants to selectively contract and release muscle groups one by one, allowing their bodies to enter into a state of deepened relaxation. As a result, participants become more aware of the difference between the feeling of tension and the feeling of relaxation.

Visualization (Mental Focus)

Visualization, or guided imagery, techniques are often used for stress management and as an aid to relaxation. Suggest peaceful images, eliciting sights, sounds, smells, and sensations that mentally transport participants to a more relaxing environment, facilitating the relaxation response.

Exercise Guidelines and Protocol

Fitness instructors have access to a variety of resources that focus on exercise design and implementation. Understanding the nature of scientific writing, as well as the research and publication process, is important in determining the accuracy and validity of the source.

Peer-reviewed journals. Generally, when one speaks of "research" or "research articles," he or she is referring specifically to articles that are published in peer-reviewed or refereed journals. Articles submitted for publication in these journals are generally descriptions of the laboratory experiment results, clinical trials, reviews of previous studies, or meta-analyses (i.e., a technique for evaluating a number of studies and drawing new conclusions based upon existing data). The editorial boards of these journals are experts in their fields and evaluate an article based of its own merit (such as sound study design and appropriate data analysis), in addition to the context of other research in a given subject area. The peer-reviewed journals are useful in identifying or analyzing new or evolving areas of thought in a particular discipline.

Articles in non-refereed journals (such as those found in consumer magazines), as well as newspaper and television stories, are sources of information for both fitness professionals and the general public. Although magazines and newspapers have editorial staffs to ensure that the information they publish is accurate, they do not have the access to expert opinion of the peer-reviewed journals, nor do they review articles in the same way. Articles in these sources tend to cover broader topics, are more often based on opinion or casual observation than scientific study, and may be influenced by commercial interests. While they can provide the fitness professional with valuable insights (especially about consumer attitudes and fitness), they are typically a good starting point for further inquiry rather than an end point in themselves.

Textbooks. For instructors seeking to build a general knowledge base (such as basic anatomy or biomechanics), a textbook or reference book may be a better source. College-level textbooks provide a balanced discussion of a given topic and will highlight areas of controversy. While textbooks bring together diverse points of view and provide consensus, they might not be as "up-to-date" as journal articles (check the copyright date).

Web-based resources. The Internet has opened the door to a multitude of resources for fitness instructors from peer-reviewed journal articles, to online courses, to educational handouts for participants, and more. However, the challenge is to locate credible sites. Look for online research articles and supportive data from acclaimed industry associations and organizations, for example: (a) American College of Sports Medicine (www.acsm.org), (b) Centers for Disease Control and Prevention (www.cdc.gov), (c) National Institute on Health (www.nih.gov and http://medlineplus.gov), and (d) U.S. Department of Health and Human Services (www.usdhh.gov). Fitness instructors can locate information addressing exercise physiology, anatomy and kinesiology, exercise programming and technique, nutrition, injury prevention, wellness, and more. Many of the sites are free to users or may require a membership fee.

Part II

Special Populations

Standards and Guidelines for the Large-Sized Participant

Standards and Guidelines for Prenatal Fitness

Standards and Guidelines for Youth Fitness

Standards and Guidelines for Senior Fitness

Part 1: Healthy Sedentary Older Adults
Part 2: Frail Elderly

2

STANDARDS and GUIDELINES for the Large-Sized Participant

I. Introduction

There are two primary goals for beginning and continuing a regular exercise program. The first is to maintain or improve the health of the body. The second is to gain enjoyment from the experience of moving the body in a pleasurable way. Historically, large-sized individuals (refers to overweight and/or overfat body types) have not felt welcomed by the fitness industry. Therefore, only a limited number of this population has been able to enjoy either of these benefits.

Many instructors have lacked the knowledge and confidence to provide safe and effective fitness programs for large-sized exercisers. Coupled with the intimidation and anxiety felt by many large people when they begin an exercise program, the number of fitness programs suited to meet the needs of this special population has been small. But a growing number of large men and women are now claiming their rightful space in fitness facilities, and they are demanding knowledgeable and unbiased instructors of all sizes to be at their sides for education and support. These standards and guidelines are provided for instructors who are willing to meet that challenge and are to be used in conjunction with AFAA's *Basic Exercise Standards and Guidelines.*

II. Fat Bias

A. Societal Bias

The bias against fat people in our society is so pervasive that very few individuals can be bias-free without conscious effort. The degradation that fat people are subjected to by themselves and others does not create a self-image conducive to health enhancement.

B. The Instructor

It is essential that fitness instructors choosing to work with large individuals address their own fat bias. Only then will they be able to see how their bias gets in the way of successful communication with their participants. The way instructors talk about their own bodies, their fears concerning being fat, their desire to make everyone thin, the types of jokes they tell—these are all behaviors they can examine to increase awareness of and manage their own bias.

C. The Health/Fitness Facility Environment

The posters, graphics, instructor exercise-wear, books, and magazines present in many health/fitness facilitiies and studios often continue the adoration of the thin, ultra-fit physique. Fitness facilities should be aware that these images do not necessarily motivate all participants, particularly those whose bodies have already demonstrated an inability to conform to this thinner ideal. Showcasing images that reflect healthy people of all sizes and shapes will make the health/fitness facility atmosphere more comfortable for the large-sized participant, and will demonstrate a recognition of the true meaning of health.

III. Application

These guidelines have been formulated to acquaint fitness instructors with the unique needs of large-sized exercisers. Because there is such a vast range of body shapes and sizes, no one rule necessarily applies to all large people. Also, because many large people are involved in a variety of sports and fitness activities, there is no intended implication that all large people are unfit.

These guidelines are designed to meet the needs of the average healthy large person participating in a group exercise class. Obviously, personal fitness trainers and instructors teaching classes of only large-sized individuals will be able to implement these recommendations to the greatest extent. While guidelines are not provided here for step classes, weighted workouts, water exercise, exercise equipment, and sports, these are all viable options for large individuals.

IV. Benefits of Consistent Exercise

The following lists of benefits of regular exercise are well documented. Keep in mind that the physiological and musculoskeletal benefits are long-term and, therefore, may be less motivating than the psychosocial benefits. Placing the initial focus of exercise programs on science and education may deprive individuals of the most valuable ingredient to long-term adherence—pleasure.

A. Physiological Benefits of Exercise
- Increased aerobic capacity
- Decreased resting heart rate
- Decreased blood pressure
- Reduced serum cholesterol and triglycerides
- Improved body composition
- Improved hormonal function

B. Musculoskeletal Benefits of Exercise
- Increased muscle strength and endurance
- Increased muscle mass
- Increased range of motion
- Improved balance
- Improved joint stability
- Improved flexibility
- Improved bone density

C. Psychosocial Benefits of Exercise
- Increased energy
- Enhanced self-esteem and feelings of well-being
- Increased feelings of self-efficacy
- Opportunity for shared activity with family and friends
- Improved sleep
- Increased self-confidence and body-esteem

V. Participant Screening

A. Medical Clearance

It is discriminatory to require a medical clearance for participation based solely on the size of the individual. Every person beginning an exercise program, regardless of size, should complete a health risk assessment (e.g., PAR-Q). The fitness instructor should follow the guidelines for medical clearance as outlined in AFAA's *Basic Exercise Standards and Guidelines*, section V.5.

B. Fitness Evaluation and Testing

The administration of any kind of fitness testing, including strength, flexibility, body composition, and cardiorespiratory endurance, unless specifically recommended by a physician, should be optional for the participant. While the results of these tests may provide motivation for some people, they may have just the opposite effect on others. The tests may take some people to the limits of their fitness abilities before they even begin, setting up a situation in which a person feels he/she must "pass" in order to participate. The instructor's primary goal should be to have participants moving as soon and as safely as possible. Fitness testing may be just one more barrier between the participant and an exercise regimen.

VI. Training Principles and Guidelines

The factors that need to be taken into consideration when personalizing an exercise program for large individuals are their: (a) size, (b) strength, (c) flexibility, (d) orthopedic limitations, and (e) health status, including the presence (if applicable) of risk factors. The participant's time schedule, exercise preferences, exercise history, and goals must also be considered.

A. The Role of the Instructor as Lifestyle Educator

1. When guiding others through the process of a healthy lifestyle change, the instructor assumes many roles: (a) facilitator, (b) coach, (c) educator, and (d) role model. Large-sized individuals are no different than anyone else in their need to be treated with respect and to be heard. Instructors must have an understanding of the process of change and the various ways their participants will go through that process. Instructors should also realize that their most important responsibility, outside of teaching a safe and effective class, is to listen, not talk.

2. The lifestyle educator has perhaps the greatest impact on motivating the large participant to adopt healthy habits. Among other things, instructors should be able to incorporate the following in their teaching experiences.
   - Maintain a professional manner that encompasses an unprejudiced and nonjudgmental attitude toward their participants.
   - Recognize individual differences in fitness and health levels.
   - Act as a role model showing exercise as just one part of a balanced mind, body, and spirit.
   - Show sincere interest in each participant and develop a rapport that leads to a relationship built on trust.
   - Identify participants who need more support or more personalized attention.
   - Show sensitivity, compassion, and patience with every participant.
   - Adapt exercise programs to meet individual needs.
   - Teach proper technique, alignment, and posture.
   - Educate the participants as to which exercises increase strength, improve cardiorespiratory function, reduce body fat, or increase flexibility.
   - Impart a positive attitude toward exercise.
   - Offer non-diet methods for changing eating behavior.

B. Goal Setting

Historically, large individuals have either been encouraged to lose weight before beginning an exercise program or their success with exercise has been linked so closely with weight loss that success with exercise seemed unachievable. When goal setting with large-sized participants, instructors should not assume that weight loss is the desired goal. The instructor should ask what each participant's goals are, provide education as to the realistic nature of the goals, and offer support for whatever the participant's chosen goals are. The instructor must be able to help the participant differentiate between exercise and eating behavior goals, so that success with one is not dependent on success with the other.

C. Intensity/Duration

See AFAA's *Basic Exercise Standards and Guidelines*, section IV.

1. Research indicates that exercise training at a moderate intensity (40–< 60% of heart rate reserve) for 30 minutes at least 5 days per week can improve health and well-being. The revised Borg Scale of Perceived Exertion is the recommended method for determining and monitoring the intensity of exercise for large individuals.

2. The location of body mass directly affects the intensity of the exercise. For example, if there is a large amount of body mass in the torso and upper extremities, exercises with arms elevated will increase the workload of the performing muscles and the cardiorespiratory system. Likewise, if there is a large amount of body mass in the hips, buttocks and lower extremities, elevating the legs (e.g., marching, knee lifts) will increase the workload.

3. It is well known that a longer duration is better for general weight loss, since more work is being performed and more calories are being burned. However, very large participants will be unable to exercise for long durations at first. It is very likely that some exercisers will only be able to sustain 5 minutes or so of cardiorespiratory conditioning. This is to be expected, and every effort to move should be applauded and encouraged. Eventually, the 5 minutes can increase to 10, then 15, 20, and so on. The ACSM recommends as much as 50–60 minutes per day on most days of the week for weight loss. It is also recommended that at least 2,000 kcals be expended through exercise each week for long-term weight control.

D. Frequency

See AFAA's *Basic Exercise Standards and Guidelines*, section IV.

An exercise frequency of at least 3 days per week is recommended at first, even if the duration is only 10–15 minutes each time. Too much, too soon is the major cause of drop-out and/or injury. A slow, gradual progression is key to success. When a participant is comfortable with three times per week, then he or she can increase the frequency to four to five times per week, keeping the intensity relatively low. Eventually, he or she can be encouraged to walk at a low intensity everyday, although once the intensity is increased, more vigorous exercise should be limited to no more than five times per week. Instructors may also consider the use of interval and intermittent training. Refer to AFAA's *Basic Exercise Standards and Guidelines*, section VIII.C., on "Cardiorespiratory Training."

E. Rate of Progression

Exercise must be of sufficient duration, intensity, frequency, and/or type to create a training effect. This training effect will usually allow participants to increase their workload gradually over time. The latest research suggests that moderate levels of exercise can produce profound health changes. For this reason, there is no need to push participants beyond their comfort level. Each participant's exercise program should be evaluated and adjusted accordingly.

F. Body Alignment/Posture/Muscle Balancing

See AFAA's *Basic Exercise Standards and Guidelines*, section VI.C.

In addition, the instructor should be particularly aware that sedentary individuals often lack the body awareness necessary for maintaining proper alignment when exercising. Common misalignments that may be obvious to the instructor on a thin person may not be as apparent on a larger person. One common misalignment in large individuals is the genu valgum posture, also known as "knock-knee," in which the tibia follows a line that goes outward from its proximal to its distal end. Instructors should educate their participants on proper alignment while remaining aware of additional stresses that occur on joints with misalignment.

G. Speed of Movement

1. Body mass may affect joint range of motion as well as the ability of arms and legs to maneuver safely through rapid movement. All movement, including stretching, strengthening, and cardiorespiratory conditioning, should be performed with control. Rapid movements that utilize momentum should be avoided, as the additional body weight may place a physiological stress on the muscles and joints similar to a weighted workout.

2. Speed of movement has a direct impact on the intensity of the exercise. As heart rate should be carefully controlled, the speed of any

movement should directly correlate with the size, shape, fitness level, and exercise experience of the individual.

3. At least initially, not all large individuals will be comfortable moving from a standing position to the floor. Options should always be made available to perform the floor exercises in a standing or seated position. If moving to the floor, extra time should be allowed for transition from a floor-to-standing position or vice versa. Raising or lowering the large body should be accomplished slowly and carefully to avoid injury and reduce anxiety.

H. Breathing

1. Breathing should follow a consistent, rhythmic pattern throughout the class to avoid an increase in blood pressure. Inhale and exhale through the nose and mouth in a relaxed fashion, always exhaling on the exertion.

2. Holding one's breath is a common problem with large exercisers, as moving or lifting additional body weight often requires extra effort. The instructor should avoid exercises that cause compression of the chest cavity (e.g., extreme forward flexion to stretch the buttocks/hamstrings) to avoid causing breathing problems.

3. Dyspnea (shortness of breath) and hyperpnea (rapid breathing), common with entry-level exercisers, may not only provoke fear and anxiety, but may also be caused by these emotions. Dyspnea and hyperpnea usually lessen or disappear over time.

4. Rapid heart rate, as it occurs in cardiorespiratory training, may be physically and emotionally uncomfortable for individuals who are experiencing it for the first time. Given the fact that most large individuals have been educated to believe they are candidates for a heart attack, the anxiety is easily understandable. The instructor should act as educator and compassionate coach in these circumstances.

I. Exercise Danger Signs

Know the exercise danger signs as outlined in AFAA's *Basic Exercise Standards and Guidelines*, section V.B.1.

As part of the pre-class instruction, participants should be advised to inform the instructor of any pain or discomfort they may experience during class. When working with entry-level exercisers, pay special attention to observing outward signs of physical distress and fatigue that could possibly lead to a more serious condition or injury.

J. Music

Research into the effects of music on exercise performance reveals energy expenditure generally increases while perceived exertion generally decreases when music accompanies exercise. Results indicate that music may act as a stimulus that takes the mind away from the physical manifestations of exercise. This may have both a positive and negative influence on the exerciser. On the positive side, music takes participants' minds off exercise, thereby allowing them to accomplish more of the workload with less awareness of discomfort or fatigue. On the negative side, this lessened awareness may cause participants to exercise too strenuously, making them more prone to injury or exceeding their recommended intensity levels. The fitness instructor, recognizing the value of music as a motivating factor, should be watchful of any indicators that a participant is overexercising as a result of involvement with the music.

K. Special Exercise Considerations

Keep in mind that an entry-level exerciser may initially have difficulty meeting the minimums of exercise frequency, intensity, and duration. The exercise training minimums should be incorporated only when the participant is physically able to accomplish them without injury, abnormally elevated heart rate, or undue muscle fatigue. To avoid these anxiety-producing consequences of overexercise, a low-intensity interval training program may be an option for certain individuals as it allows the instructor to alternate exercises that sustain a higher heart rate with those that do not. Balance participants' fitness levels with their comfort levels.

VII. Class Format

A. Sequence

See AFAA's *Basic Exercise Standards and Guidelines*, section VII.
Sequence takes on greater importance with large exercisers as transitioning from floor to standing is not always easily accomplished. It may be preferable in some cases to conduct the entire class in a standing or chair-seated position to avoid the strain of lifting the body and lowering it to the floor. If floorwork is included, avoid a great deal of floor-to-standing transitions.

B. Types of Movement

1. Aerobic exercise, which utilizes the large muscle groups and is rhythmical in nature, benefits the cardiorespiratory system and improves body composition. Muscle strengthening exercises increase lean body mass and have a positive effect on body composi-

tion profiles. The large skeletal muscles are avid calorie consumers, so an increase in muscle mass has an impact on overall energy expenditure. Cardiorespiratory conditioning exercises contribute to the maintenance of lean tissue, while strengthening exercises build lean tissue.

2. Physical limitations for large exercisers are not necessarily different from those of thin people, nor are large exercisers more prone to injury in class. Orthopedic problems that the fitness instructor may encounter in participants include arthritis, as well as lower back, hip, knee, and ankle joint discomfort. In the presence of pain or discomfort, weight-bearing activities may be alternated with non-weight-bearing activities as a method of avoiding stress on the joints.

3. Research shows that while large exercisers usually have good motor coordination, their additional weight can make balance a limiting factor in exercise performance, comfort and enjoyment. The class format should, therefore, include exercises that improve body awareness and balance. A common concern among large people is the fear of falling down during exercise. This often comes from a lack of trust that they can move their large bodies safely. These fears should dissipate over time. In the meantime, supported balance exercises (e.g., using a wall or ballet barre) and kinesthetic awareness exercises (e.g., touching the biceps as they contract) may help to build confidence and allay fears.

VIII. Recommendations for Instructors

•   For both psychological and physiological reasons, attending an exercise class may be a stressful experience for the large person that is new to exercise. The instructor should be cognizant of this and should try, by listening and reassuring, to alleviate as much stress as possible.

•   The fitness instructor should recognize that participation in an exercise program is often the first step toward a more comprehensive lifestyle change. The instructor should be responsive to the participant's need for support and encouragement. The instructor should be prepared to refer the participant to reputable professionals in other health professions (e.g., nutrition, stress management).

•   The instructor should give clear, concise instructions in every class for each exercise. Describe the exercises "generically" (e.g., "Reach toward your feet" rather than "Hold onto your feet") to accommodate the variety of strength and flexibility levels in the class.

•   In the initial stages of training, exercises that are easily accomplished may be preferable to those that offer a challenge. Feelings of inadequacy are thereby avoided and the participant's confidence in his/her ability to succeed in this endeavor begins to build at the outset.

- Entry-level exercisers may prefer exercises that are repetitive over a period of time so they are able to notice immediate improvements in coordination, strength, flexibility, and confidence.
- Not all exercises are recommended for the large exerciser as some movements may be awkward to perform or inappropriate for the larger body size or shape. Exercise selection should be based on the instructor's knowledge of each class participant.
- Stretch out more often than usual. This helps to dispel any associations participants may make between exercise and discomfort. It also provides a pertinent break between more strenuous exercises.
- There are no specific exercises that can or should be done by larger people. The key to appropriate fitness programming is to learn how to modify exercises for each individual based on the answers to the following five questions for that individual.
  - What is the most effective position in which to work this muscle group considering the weight distribution?
  - Is the spine protected?
  - What is the leverage to be considered?
  - What is a reasonable speed of movement?
  - What is a reasonable range of motion?

IX. Pre-Class Instruction

A. Pre-Class Announcements

See AFAA's *Basic Exercise Standards and Guidelines*, section VIII.A.

B. Participant Expectations of an Exercise Program

A major factor for maintaining long-term adherence (6 months or longer) in an exercise program is a realistic set of expectations. External physical results usually follow long after internal physiological and psychological results. To avoid discouragement with exercise, it is incumbent on the instructor to educate the large exerciser concerning the expected results of exercise and a realistic time frame for seeing or feeling the manifestations of these results. While research cannot yet confirm exact times or results, a fair analysis of data indicates that the first conditioning effects may be visible 6–12 weeks into a consistent exercise program. It may be of more importance to large participants to focus on their ability to move and breathe with greater ease as well as the actions they've been taking to accomplish that ability. They should also be encouraged to focus on the pleasure of movement. The instructor should NOT pitch exercise as just another means of quick weight loss because it will encourage participants to adopt a diet mentality around exercise (e.g., all-or-nothing thinking, feelings of failure, a need to be thin in order to succeed, attempts to be perfect).

C. Skin Abrasions

Fitness instructors should be aware that some large exercisers may experience skin irritation due to chafing. Participants should be advised to closely monitor areas where skin irritation might occur (e.g., inside of thighs). If the problem is chronic, medical attention should be sought.

D. Attire

1. The importance of wearing shoes appropriate to the activity is now well understood. This is especially true for large exercisers who also depend on shoes for added stability. Additional factors affecting shoe selection may include adequate ventilation and shoe width. Participants should be advised that their shoes are likely to wear out faster and should be replaced more often.

2. Many large women are uncomfortable wearing revealing exercise clothes. Inappropriate workout clothes, however, are uncomfortable and may affect exercise performance by causing heat stress (e.g., polyester fabrics that don't breathe or long-sleeved sweats that are too warm). There is finally a greater selection of workout clothes available for large exercisers. A list of stores and catalogues with exercise-wear for large men and women should be made available to every new large participant. Participants should be encouraged to wear fabrics that breathe (e.g., cotton). Choice of attire should also reflect environment and temperature/humidity.

See AFAA's *Basic Exercise Standards and Guidelines*, section VIII.B.

X. Warm-Up

A. Special Considerations

1. Psychological preparation should be incorporated into the warm-up by means of gradual movements and verbal motivation from the instructor.

2. Emphasis should be placed on dynamic movements that utilize the large muscle groups through their full range of motion.

3. Special attention should be given to properly preparing the lower back, and shoulder, hip, knee, and ankle joints for the more vigorous exercises to follow.

4. Include exercises that improve body awareness and balance. For participants who are just beginning exercise training, utilize support for the balancing exercises.

B. Precautions

1. Select a speed of movement that allows participants to achieve full range of motion without momentum.
2. Supported forward flexion should not compress the chest or abdominal area to the point that it inhibits breathing.
3. If there is a greater amount of body mass in the medial deltoid area, do not force the arm toward the ear as it may lead to dizziness.
4. Warm-up should be accomplished in a standing or chair-seated position.
5. Exercise selection should be congruent with the fitness level of the participants.
6. Elbow and knee joint hyperextension should be avoided.

See AFAA's *Basic Exercise Standards and Guidelines*, section VIII.C.

XI. Cardiorespiratory Training

A. Special Considerations

1. Low-impact aerobics, walking, and water fitness are a few recommended methods for attaining cardiorespiratory conditioning.
2. Low-impact aerobics significantly lessens the amount of stress normally associated with high-impact aerobics.
3. When performing low-impact aerobics:
   - start slowly and gradually increase the intensity and range of motion of the movements. Movements should be controlled, resistive, and non-ballistic.
   - arm and leg elevation should be varied to control heart rate and reduce the stress on joints.
   - leg elevation should directly correlate to the flexibility, strength, and fitness level of the participant.
   - combination moves requiring coordination of both arms and legs should be entered into slowly, starting with either the arms or the legs and then adding the other in order to build in positive experiences with movement.

B. Precautions

1. Entry-level exercisers often have difficulty pacing themselves. Watch for signs of overexertion.

2. Do not include movements that rely strictly on momentum for execution.

3. High-impact aerobics is inappropriate for most large exercisers. Certain large people who have been participating in a consistent exercise program of walking or low-impact aerobics, and are free of orthopedic problems, may gradually begin a high-impact aerobics program.

4. Some lateral movements may be difficult for certain large participants. Always offer a side-step alternative.

5. Avoid movements that require quick turns unless the movements are executed at such a slow speed that large participants will not risk torquing their knees or ankles to complete them.

6. Avoid movements that may result in slipping, twisting the ankles, or hyperextending the joints.

C. Monitoring Intensity

Fatty deposits in the area of the wrist and neck make pulse monitoring the least effective method of evaluating exercise intensity. Additionally, heart rate monitor chest straps may be too small and/or inaccurate due to fat mass. The preferred method for intensity monitoring is the Borg Rating of Perceived Exertion (RPE) Scale. On the 0 to 10 scale, the recommended level is 4–6 (moderate to somewhat hard); on the 6 to 20 scale, the recommended level is 12–14. Remember that overly-deconditioned people may become anxious and stressed when they feel their heart rate beating rapidly, and they may have difficulty pacing themselves. It is best to help them avoid over exercising and overexertion.

See AFAA's *Basic Exercise Standards and Guidelines*, section VIII.C.3.

XII. Cool-Down

A. Special Considerations
For entry-level exercisers, a longer cool-down is recommended.

B. Precautions
Use the Borg Scale of Perceived Exertion to monitor the participant's intensity level following the cool-down period. If the participant still identifies an intensity of "moderate" or higher, he/she should be advised to work at a lower intensity. See AFAA's *Fitness: Theory & Practice* (5th edition), Chapter 20, "Monitoring Exercise Intensity."

XIII. Upper Body Strengthening Exercises

See AFAA's *Basic Exercise Standards and Guidelines*, section VIII.D.

A. Special Considerations

1. Weakness in the upper body is common in inactive large participants, especially women, due to poorly developed and atrophied muscles.

2. Movements should be resistive, smooth, controlled, and slow enough to allow for complete extension.

3. Free weights (or other resistive equipment) may be used to bring about a more rapid muscular strength response. Free weights should only be introduced once the participant is able to complete a non-weighted workout with controlled contraction and without undue fatigue. Utilization of free weights should begin with the lowest weight, adding additional weight only when the participant is able to complete 8–10 repetitions in the same range of motion without undue fatigue.

4. The decision to incorporate push-ups should be based on the participant's strength and orthopedic limitations, as push-ups on the floor increase stress on the shoulders and wrists. Weight-supported modifications (e.g., doing push-ups against the wall from a standing position) lessen the stress and may be more appropriate in the initial stages of training.

B. Precautions

1. When there is a greater amount of body mass in the arms, leverage is the key factor in the safe and effective performance of upper body work. Large individuals should be instructed to perform short lever movements if fatigue sets in or if momentum begins to replace slow, resistive movement.

2. If standing, elbow and knee joints should not be hyperextended.

3. Vary the arm elevation, lever length, and range of motion to avoid early fatigue and stress on the joints.

See AFAA's *Basic Exercise Standards and Guidelines*, section VIII.D.

XIV. Legs, Hips, and Buttocks Strengthening Exercises

A. Special Considerations

1. In many cases, the lower body, excluding the abdomen, has undergone a slow, progressive strength adaptation to accommodate a larger individual's increased body weight. The instructor may, therefore, see greater muscular strength and endurance in the performance of lower body exercises.

2. For hip abduction in the side-lying position, the upper body should be totally supported in a comfortable position. Depending on body mass distribution, there are three positions to choose from: (a) the torso is lying fully extended on the floor, (b) the torso is raised up on one elbow with the head supported by the hand, or (c) the torso is raised up on one elbow with the supporting hand placed flat on the floor. The instructor should educate the participants as to the position options, and guide them toward choosing the most comfortable position in which they can also maintain alignment.

3. It is difficult to achieve significant range of motion performing hip adduction in the side-lying position with the top leg in front if there is great body mass in the inner thigh area. An alternate position is with the foot of the top leg placed behind the working leg, as long as there is no torque on the knee or ankle and body mass in the buttocks can support the spine.

4. During the initial stages of training, the all-fours position for gluteals and hamstrings should be performed with the upper body resting on the elbows rather than on the hands. This position improves balance, decreases the amount of weight that needs to be supported, and reduces the risk of spinal hyperextension due to the pull of gravity.

5. Hip adduction in the supine position should be performed with both feet placed on the floor if: (a) a greater amount of body mass in the hips, buttocks, and lower extremities makes it difficult to keep the back on the floor; or (b) a lack of strength makes it difficult to keep both elevated legs at a 90° angle to the body.

6. Standing leg lifts to strengthen quadriceps should be performed with support (e.g., wall, ballet barre).

B. Precautions

1. If not performed properly, squats and lunges may place stress on the knees. Use a chair for support and work within the participants' range of motion.

2. When there is a greater amount of body mass in the lower body, leverage is the key factor in the safe and effective performance of lower body work for large individuals. Participants should be instructed to work with a short lever if fatigue sets in or if momentum begins to replace slow, resistive movement.

XV. Abdominal Strengthening Exercises

See AFAA's *Basic Exercise Standards and Guidelines*, section VIII.D.

A. Special Considerations

1. Large individuals with considerable abdominal mass are likely to have great difficulty performing effective abdominal exercises in the supine position due to limited range of motion and an increased workload. The extra layers of fat make it nearly impossible to feel the muscles contracting. The instructor should teach body awareness and emphasize contraction rather than lifting in the initial stages of exercise training.

2. The decision to incorporate partial abdominal curls in the supine position should be based on the participant's strength and the presence of abdominal mass that might limit range of motion. Weight-supported modifications (e.g., holding on to a towel wrapped behind the legs to assist with a lift in the supine position) may be appropriate.

3. Standing abdominal exercises are an ideal modification for participants who choose not to perform abdominal strengthening in the supine position. There are two recommended exercises: (a) spinal rotation, and (b) the standing crunch. Both exercises should be performed slowly, with conscious resistive contraction.

4. Abdominal strengthening exercises may be performed in the all-fours position on hands and knees. Participants should be instructed to contract the abdominals up toward the spine or ceiling and then relax them without allowing the spine to lose alignment on the relaxation phase.

B. Precautions

1. Breathing is especially important when performing abdominal exercises. As supine abdominal work involves, by its nature, a degree of compression to the chest cavity, care should be taken to move slowly enough so breathing is not inhibited. Holding one's breath is common among large participants during abdominal strengthening. The instructor should make frequent reminders to exhale on the exertion.

2. The participant should be advised not to rely on momentum to lift the shoulders off the floor. Additionally, all movement should be slow enough that the participant is able to physically identify a "start" and "stop" to each partial curl-up.

3. Support for the head should be incorporated on an individual basis as needed. The flexibility of the participant may not allow

for a comfortable hands-behind-the-head position. If additional support is needed, offer the participant a pillow or folded towel to place under his/her head to prevent it from falling out of alignment.

See AFAA's *Basic Exercise Standards and Guidelines*, section VIII.E.

XVI. Final Stretches /Heart Rate

A. Special Considerations

1. Many sedentary large individuals experience chronic back discomfort. Including stretches for the upper and lower back may help relieve some of this discomfort, while providing participants with the tools for alleviating discomfort on their own. This process also helps the participant associate exercise with good feelings, both physically and emotionally.

2. Participants with flexibility limitations due to greater abdominal or lower body mass may enhance their stretches with the use of props (e.g., holding on to a towel wrapped around the foot for a supine hamstring stretch).

B. Precaution

Exercise selection should take into consideration the flexibility and location of body mass of each class participant. The instructor should be prepared to offer modifications for all stretches.

STANDARDS and GUIDELINES for
Prenatal Fitness

3

I. Introduction

During the past 30 years, the United States has experienced a fitness revolution. Record numbers of people, spending millions of dollars, have sought the benefits of exercise. Coinciding with this upsurge of interest in keeping fit has been an increase in the number of women entering the workplace and pursuing careers. Consequently, many women now approach their pregnancies as they would a timeline for a special project at work. From conception through delivery, every step of the pregnancy is planned for maximum returns—a healthy baby, an efficient delivery, and a quick return to the pre-pregnancy body. A perceived determinant in achieving these goals is the health and fitness level of the mother-to-be. Many women today see exercise during pregnancy as an integral part of their prenatal program. To ensure positive experiences and outcomes, expectant mothers should familiarize themselves with the following.

1. The goal of an exercise program prescribed in conjunction with pregnancy is to maintain the highest level of fitness consistent with the participant's pre-pregnancy fitness level and the maximum safety for both mother and child.

2. Pregnancy is usually the most physiologically stressful period of a woman's life. A safe and effective fitness program performed before, during, and after pregnancy can help in the body's adjustment to the various stages and may help prevent permanent problems, including lower back strain or weakened pelvic floor muscles.

3. Weight loss should not be a goal during pregnancy. However, exercise may be useful as part of a complete prenatal program in preventing excessive weight gain.

4. Exercise during pregnancy does not guarantee a/an:
   - pregnancy free from discomfort or obstetrical complications;
   - shorter, easier labor;
   - uncomplicated delivery with reduced incidence of cesarean section; or
   - healthier baby.

With these goals in mind, AFAA, through the research of many respected individuals in the fields of obstetrics, exercise science, and fitness instruction, established the following standards and guidelines for safe and effective exercise programming for expectant mothers. These guidelines are designed to be used in conjunction with AFAA's *Basic Exercise Standards and Guidelines.*

II. Benefits of Prenatal Exercise

A. Physiological Benefits of Exercise

- Increased aerobic capacity
- Improved circulation
- Improved digestion and elimination
- Improved energy and endurance
- More restful sleep
- Better control of weight gain and fat disposition

B. Musculoskeletal Benefits of Exercise

- Improved muscular strength and endurance to help support joints and increase muscular efficiency during labor and delivery
- Increased range of motion
- Improved balance
- Improved flexibility and mobility
- Improved posture and possible prevention of permanent postural deviation and associated discomforts
- Improved support of pelvic organs

C. Psychosocial Benefits of Exercise

- Reduced tension, anxiety, and fatigue
- Enhanced feeling of well-being
- Improved self-image
- Opportunity for shared activity with family, friends, and other pregnant women
- Improved physical control over the body increases confidence in an otherwise uncontrollable situation.
- Deep relaxation exercises assist in establishing a stronger conditioned response to control discomforts of labor.

III. Participant Screening

A. Medical Clearance

All individuals beginning an exercise program should follow the guidelines for medical clearance as stated in AFAA's *Basic Exercise Standards and Guidelines*, section V. Additionally, to avoid risk of injury to participants and litigative risk to instructors, attendance in class should be limited to those with a physician's written approval. The primary responsibility for the health management of the woman's pregnancy should lie with her physician. The decision of when to commence and when to cease an exercise program rests with the physician. A close alliance between the fitness instructor and the participant's physician is strongly recommended.

B. Health-Risk Appraisal

It is important to evaluate an individual's level of fitness prior to commencement of an exercise program to:

- determine the current level of physical fitness and overall health status;
- objectively evaluate an individual's response to exercise; and
- determine an appropriate workload when individualizing an exercise regimen.

Only qualified specialists (e.g., health care providers) may assess the safety of exercise, administer an exercise stress test, and write an exercise program for the prospective prenatal exercise class participant. It is again recommended that all class participants have written approval from their physician, and instructors obtain health histories on prospective participants to learn of any limitations and make sure exercise level is appropriate. It should be noted that health histories taken by a physician may fail to reveal prior orthopedic problems and postural deviations. Due to the added weight gain associated with pregnancy, evaluation of any orthopedic condition is important. Questions related to prior orthopedic or postural problems should be included in the questionnaire. Refer any questions to the woman's physician.

C. Role of the Instructor

1. Instructors need to be cognizant of the fact that for both physiological and psychological reasons, attending an exercise class may be a stressful experience for a pregnant exerciser. Therefore, try to reassure, educate, and communicate with the participant and her physician to alleviate stress and increase comfort level in classes.

2. A discussion regarding the goals and realistic expectations of an exercise program should be conducted with each class participant.

3. Specific skills for instructors teaching pregnant exercisers include the following.

   a. Maintaining a professional attitude that encompasses an unprejudiced and nonjudgmental attitude toward participants.

   b. Demonstrating sincere interest in developing a trusting rapport with each participant.

   c. Recognizing individual differences in fitness and health levels.

   d. Adapting exercise programs to meet individual needs.

    e. Being sensitive to the participants' needs and helping them establish realistic goals.

    f. Identifying participants who need more support or more personalized attention.

    g. Showing sensitivity, patience, and personal interest in each woman and her pregnancy.

    h. Remembering the body sensitivity of pregnant women and wearing conservative fitness attire.

    i. Respecting your own area of expertise and that of other professionals by making referrals at all times when questions arise outside your professional experience and education.

D. Exercise Contraindications

1. Absolute Contraindications
   - Hemodynamically significant heart disease
   - Restrictive lung disease
   - Incompetent cervix
   - Multiple gestations at risk for premature labor
   - Persistent second or third trimester bleeding
   - Placenta previa after 26 weeks of gestation
   - Premature labor during the current pregnancy
   - Ruptured membranes
   - Pregnancy-induced hypertension (PIH)/Pre-eclampsia

2. Relative Contraindications
   - Severe anemia
   - Unevaluated maternal cardiac dysrhythmia
   - Chronic bronchitis
   - Poorly controlled type 1 diabetes
   - Extreme morbid obesity
   - Extreme underweight (BMI < 12)
   - History of extremely sedentary lifestyle
   - Intrauterine growth restriction in current pregnancy
   - Poorly controlled hypertension
   - Orthopedic limitations
   - Poorly controlled seizure disorder
   - Poorly controlled hyperthyroidism
   - Heavy smoker

IV. Class Format, Exercise Recommendations, and Professional Responsibilities

A. Sequence

1. Depending upon the class type and objectives, formats will vary. AFAA recommends every class include the following components.
   a. Pre-class announcements
   b. Warm-up activity preparation period
   c. Body of the workout (e.g., cardio, strength, flexibility training)
   d. Post-exercise relaxation, stretching, and/or cool-down
2. Additional considerations for pregnant participants include the following.
   a. Changing position from one exercise to another and getting up and down off of the floor takes additional time and effort.
   b. Performing specific muscular toning exercises prior to cardiovascular training may fatigue large muscle groups, rendering the cardiorespiratory segment difficult and possibly increasing risk of injury.
   c. Include specific exercises for strengthening the pelvic floor early in pregnancy.
      1) Weight of the uterus places tremendous downward pressure on the pelvic floor.
      2) Weak muscles may cause stress, urinary incontinence, postnatal sexual dysfunction, and uterine prolapse.

B. Types of Movement

1. Avoid rapid twisting and directional changes because of painful pull on round ligaments.
   a. Maintain torso stabilization with hips and shoulders facing forward in neutral spine when performing lateral movements.
2. Displaced center of gravity increases risk of losing balance.
   a. Perform movements at a moderate pace, which allows for careful transition from one direction to another.
3. Describe transitions and cueing well in advance for exercise or directional changes.
   a. Always make sure the upper body is supported and stable before moving.
   b. When moving from a sitting to a standing position, utilize the following procedure.
      1) Support body with hand on floor as weight is transferred to knee.
      2) Bring other foot forward.
      3) Support body weight on top of thigh when coming to a full standing position.

          4)   Move feet right away.

          5)   Reverse procedure when moving from a standing to a sitting position.

      c.   When moving from a sitting to a side-lying position, utilize the following procedure.

          1)   Roll to the side onto the hip and walk the body down with hands, arms supporting upper body weight.

          2)   Reverse when moving from a side-lying position on the floor to a sitting position.

    4.   Transitions from standing to floor and vice versa should be performed carefully.

    5.   Modifications for low-impact aerobics are as follows.

      a.   The traditional large, low down-up step patterns performed in low-impact aerobics can cause pelvic floor pressure, knee stress, and compromised balance. Modify these movements by reducing down-up motion and incorporating more traveling movements instead.

      b.   Include both long and short-range movements of the upper body to avoid excessive stress on the shoulder joints.

C. Frequency

Participants new to exercise should begin with three workouts per week and add additional workouts only after adaptation to the current program has occurred. More frequent training requires careful monitoring for signs of overtraining or complications of pregnancy. Regular prenatal care is recommended.

D. Rate of Progression

1. Pregnancy is a time to maintain fitness, not strive for dramatic improvements. As body weight increases, workload will normally decrease.

2. Participants new to exercise may be able to increase workload slightly at start of program.

E. Posture and Alignment

Instructors should be aware that a woman's center of gravity becomes displaced during pregnancy, and maintaining proper posture and alignment becomes progressively more difficult.

1. Pelvic Tilt—is used as an exercise in various positions to help maintain neutral pelvic alignment and alleviate back stress during pregnancy.

a. Participants should follow the basic guidelines for maintaining proper body alignment found in AFAA's *Basic Exercise Standards and Guidelines*, section VI.C.

b. Encourage pregnant participants to maintain neutral pelvic alignment in all positions (e.g., sitting, standing, on all fours, side-lying, and while moving). This may help ease associated discomfort, particularly in the lower back, and may help prevent permanent postural problems.

2. Method
   a. Slowly release pelvis.
   b. Slowly return pelvis to starting position by contracting both abdominals and gluteals.
   c. Pelvic floor muscles should also be contracted.

3. Precautions
   a. Do not bear down on pelvic floor, as this can contribute to vaginal varicosities.
   b. Perform this exercise in a slow, controlled manner. Throwing the pelvis back or rapidly arching the back may strain the lumbar spine.

F. Breathing

The uterus crowding the diaphragm may cause frequent feelings of dyspnea.

1. Breathing in a consistent rhythmic pattern throughout the class to avoid an increase in blood pressure. Inspire and expire through the nose and mouth in a relaxed fashion, always exhaling on the exertion. Reminders to breathe rhythmically should be made throughout the class.

2. Holding one's breath can elicit the Valsalva maneuver, which can increase intra-abdominal pressure.

G. Exercise Danger Signs

1. Exercise Danger Signs as outlined in AFAA's *Basic Exercise Standards and Guidelines*, section V.B.

2. Safety in Prenatal Exercise*—Pregnant exercisers should have a clear understanding of how to monitor exercise intensity. They should not feel exhausted throughout the day from an exercise session. In addition, they need to be made aware of the warning signs for health risks. Signs and symptoms indicating immediate cessation of exercise and referral to physician's care include:
   a. Pain of any kind—chest, head, back, pubic, or hip

      b.   Uterine contractions (frequent at 20-minute intervals)

      c.   Vaginal bleeding, leaking of amniotic fluid

      d.   Dizziness and/or faintness

      e.   Shortness of breath

      f.   Palpitation, tachycardia

      g.   Persistent nausea and vomiting

      h.   Difficulty walking, calf pain or swelling, and/or muscle weakness

      i.   Generalized edema

      j.   Decreased fetal activity

*When working with pregnant exercisers, special attention must be paid to observing outward signs of physical distress and fatigue that can possibly lead to a more dangerous condition.

3.   Hydration and Heat Loss—Pregnant women are not as efficient as non-pregnant women at exchanging heat. During pregnancy women tend to store fat, which insulates and decreases heat loss. Core temperature increases, this is why most pregnant women are warmer. Sustaining vigorous activity (20–30 minutes) increases body core temperature. However, benefits of training include a partial acclimatization to the increased core temperature and, therefore, sweating occurs sooner which lowers core temperature. Participants should be encouraged to hydrate before, during, and after exercise despite concern with urinary frequency (refer to AF-AA's *Basic Exercise Standards and Guidelines*, V.B.6.). Dehydration, increasing core temperature to dangerous levels, has been known to precipitate premature labor. Adequate hydration and re-hydration is especially important in a swimming pool where participants do not notice when and how much they might be sweating. Checking the urine can also indicate hydration status. Normal urine is a clear, pale yellow. A dark, concentrated yellow can indicate the mother is not getting enough fluid.

H. Music

Research into the effect of music on exercise performance reveals energy expenditure generally increases while perceived exertion generally decreases when music accompanies exercise. These results may indicate that music acts as a stimulus that takes the mind away from the physical manifestations of exercise. Although this enhances the enjoyment of exercise, lack of awareness may cause a participant to exercise too strenuously, making her more prone to injury or exceeding her training heart rate. The fitness instructor should be observant of any indicators that a participant is overexercising as a result of involvement with the music. Play music slightly slower for the pregnant exerciser because of displaced center of gravity and the resulting risk of imbalance and added weight. This will decrease the tendency to move too quickly, which can cause falling and other injury. Recommendations for beats per minute (bpm) include the following.

1. Warm-up: 120–134 bpm
2. Cardiorespiratory*: low-impact (125–145 bpm), step training (118–122 bpm), aqua fitness (124–136 bpm)
3. Muscular strength and conditioning: 120–130 bpm
4. Flexibility: under 100 bpm

*NOTE: Cardiorespiratory beats per minute ranges are slightly lower than for the average healthy adult participant.

V. Pre-Class Announcements

A. Introduction

Instructors need to introduce themselves and announce type, level, and format of the class. New participants need to be reminded to work at an intensity level appropriate for daily energy levels. Make sure participants understand how to monitor their own intensity levels.

B. Reemphasize

1. The importance of consistent physician-directed prenatal care.
2. The exercise danger signs outlined in section IV.G above.

C. Special Clothing Requirements

1. All participants should wear lightweight, non-restrictive clothing. Some participants may be more comfortable in stretch pants and T-shirts rather than tights and leotards.
2. Support tights designed for pregnancy may help improve circulation to the lower legs. (Use caution in warmer climates.)
3. A supportive bra included in all workout attire will help with the weight of enlarging breasts.
4. Some participants are more comfortable using a pregnancy belt worn under maternity tops for more support during exercise.
5. Avoid wearing vinyl clothing as this material retains body heat.
6. Wear proper shoes with support appropriate for the chosen exercise program. Examples include a cross-trainer for group exercise or aqua shoes for the pool.

D. Review of Special Exercise Considerations

1. Review section IV.A-F above with all new participants.

VI. Warm-Up

A. Definition, Purpose, and Duration
See AFAA's *Basic Exercise Standards and Guidelines*, section VIII.B.1.

B. Methods
See AFAA's *Basic Exercise Standards and Guidelines*, section VIII.B.2.

C. Special Considerations
See AFAA's *Basic Exercise Standards and Guidelines*, section VIII.B.3.

1. Due to increased weight and displaced center of gravity, start out with gentle limbering movements that gradually increase in range of motion and intensity. A fast warm-up with prolonged arm movements above shoulder height may elevate the heart rate too quickly.

2. Include rhythmic limbering movements and preparatory stretches for the lower leg and foot. This will increase circulation to the lower extremities and perhaps decrease edema.

3. Movements and stretches for hip flexors and the low back performed in an upright standing position may be easier for pregnant participants.

4. Avoid prolonged motionless standing as this can decrease cardiac output. For example, keep the legs moving while performing upper body stretches or limbering exercises.

D. Precautions

1. Unsupported forward spinal flexion can be extremely hazardous to the lumbar spine due to the downward gravitational pull of the weighted uterus.

2. Participants ought to be cautioned against movements that require excessive bouncing or jarring. (See section IV.B. above.)

VII. Cardiorespiratory Training

A. Definition, Purpose, and Duration
See AFAA's *Basic Exercise Standards and Guidelines*, section VIII.C.1.

B. Methods

1. Although AFAA's *Basic Exercise Standards and Guidelines* utilize four models of cardiorespiratory exercise, the recommendation for pregnant participants is the continuous or steady state training model.

2. Cardiorespiratory exercises are performed to gradually increase intensity, held in a steady state for the majority of the workout, and then gradually decrease.

3. ACOG recommends beginning with as little as 5 minutes of activity a day and adding 5 minutes more per week, so pregnant women can stay active up to 30 minutes a day.

4. Choreography is developed to keep the heart rate at a certain level within the target heart rate range. Movements are controlled and non-ballistic.

5. For information on fitness modalities refer to Chapter 10, "Application of Pregnancy Guidelines for Fitness Modalities," in AFAA's *Prenatal Fitness Self-Study* course manual.

C. Special Considerations

1. Intensity
   a. Heart rate
      1) Resting heart rate may increase as much as 10–15 bpm during pregnancy.
      2) Pregnant women reach maximum cardiac output at a lower level of work than non-pregnant women.
      3) ACOG guidelines emphasize the need to listen to one's own maternal symptoms, and if unable to talk normally while exercising then the chosen activity is too strenuous. (See the next section below on perceived exertion.)
   b. Perceived exertion
      1) Perceived exertion is the best indicator of workload tolerance during both cardiorespiratory training and recovery.
      2) Train at similar intensity (physiological strain), not same workload.
      3) Train at the "somewhat hard" level on the Borg rating of perceived exertion (RPE) scale. For the prenatal exerciser, perceived exertion is the best indicator of exercise intensity. The simple "talk test" may also be encouraged—if the participant is too winded to speak in short sentences, she is pushing herself too hard. If she can sing without becoming breathless, she can probably increase her intensity.

Rating of Perceived Exertion Scales			
6–20-Point RPE Scale		**Revised 10-Point RPE Scale**	
Rating	Description	Rating	Description
6		0	Nothing
7	Very, very light	0.5	Very, very light (just noticeable)
8		1	Very light
9	Very light	2	Light (weak)
10		3	Moderate
11	Fairly light	4	Somewhat hard
12		5	Heavy (strong)
13	Somewhat hard	6	
14		7	Very heavy (strong)
15	Hard	8	
16		9	
17	Very hard	10	Very, very heavy (almost max)
18			
19	Very, very hard		
20			

Reprinted with permission from "Psychological Bases of Physical Exertion" by Gunnar Borg, 1982, *Medicine & Science in Sports & Exercise.* 14 (377-381).

During pregnancy, the intensity of exercise should be light to moderate, or approximately 12 to 14 on the 6–20-point RPE scale, or 2 to 3 on the 10-point RPE scale.

c. If the pregnant exerciser has been performing regular cardiorespiratory exercise for at least 6 months prior to pregnancy, she may continue her current program provided she is monitored by a physician and experiences no discomfort or danger signs. If the current duration is maintained, reduce the intensity to the levels stated above.

D. Additional Precautions

1. Make sure pregnant exercisers know how to monitor their workloads at a comfortable pace throughout the class.

2. New exercisers often have difficulty pacing their fitness program. Be alert for signs of overexertion.

3. Monitor intensity every 4–5 minutes during the cardiorespiratory conditioning.

E. Cardiorespiratory Cool-Down (Post-Aerobic)

Recovery heart rate should return to normal levels by slowly reducing cardiorespiratory activity. Pregnant women may require a longer time to allow for sufficient heart rate recovery. Time can be from 5–10 minutes. Recovery heart rate (how quickly one attains pre-exercise rate) is a good indicator of whether or not the individual was exercising at appropriate intensity.

1. The post-aerobic cool-down heart rate may become more variable in the last trimester.

2. This is a good time for participants to visit the restroom and take a drink of cool water (approximately 8 ounces).

VIII. Muscular Strength and Endurance Training

A. Definition, Purpose, and Duration

See AFAA's *Basic Exercise Standards and Guidelines*, section VIII.D.1.

B. Methods

See AFAA's *Basic Exercise Standards and Guidelines*, section VIII.D.2.

C. Special Considerations for Pregnancy

1. Strengthening the muscles of the arms, chest, shoulders, and upper back can help prevent kyphosis and other postural deviations. Added weight of the breasts and stress of carrying an infant in the arms renders strengthening of the upper body extremely important if muscular strain is to be avoided.

2. During resistance training, participants should select a weight that permits multiple repetitions (i.e., 12–15 repetitions to be performed to a point of moderate fatigue).

3. Holding one's breath should be avoided. See section IV.F. above for specific breathing guidelines.

4. Perform exercises using resistive, smooth, controlled movements, slow enough to allow for complete range of motion.

5. Where appropriate, in a standing position, keep the legs moving with simple movements to increase circulation to the lower legs.

6. The all-fours position may be difficult during pregnancy for the following reasons.
   a. Enlarged uterus causes increased pull on the lower back and hips.
   b. Supporting body weight on the wrists may aggravate carpal tunnel syndrome.
   c. Enlarged uterus may cause pressure on the diaphragm.
   d. Maintaining proper hip alignment while abducting or extending the leg is more difficult as the pregnancy progresses.

7. After the first trimester and no more than 20 gestational weeks, omit exercises performed in the supine position.

8. Stabilization exercises are recommended with caution after the first 20 weeks of gestation because of the stress to the shoulders, back, and round ligaments, which place strain on the torso. Considerations for these exercises include a participant's skill level and active participation in regular exercise prior to pregnancy (e.g., planks, hovers, reverse planks, supine bridge, side planks, non-supported hip flexion, V-sits, single leg squats).

Group One—Chest: Pectorals

a. Push-ups—After the first trimester, perform push-ups in a standing position against a wall. Traditional push-ups on the floor may be difficult because of the gravitational pull of the weighted uterus against the low back. Placing body weight on the wrists aggravates risk of carpal tunnel syndrome, or places too much stress on the shoulders (e.g., hover).
b. Cue participants to keep wrist in neutral alignment when using small poundage of weights or tubing. Many women have had reactions to latex material. Therefore, resistive equipment with handles is recommended.
c. Stabilization exercises—see section VIII.C.7 above.
d. Sample exercises include flys, chest press with variations, and use of resistive tools.

Group Two—Back: Trapezius/Rhomboids/Latissimus Dorsi

a. Shoulder and back precaution—in a standing position cue participants for proper alignment to maintain healthy shoulders and backs. Omit performing exercises during which the shoulder abducts and internally rotates, with the elbow higher than the shoulder (e.g., upright rows). This may cause shoulder impingement. Use one hand to support the torso in the bent-over alignment position (e.g., rows, reverse flys). As weight and growth of the uterus progresses, it may be difficult to maintain torso stabilization in a non-supported hip-flexed position.
b. Cue participants to keep wrist in neutral alignment when using resistive tubes. Many women have had reactions to latex materials. Therefore, resistive tubes with handles are recommended (e.g., seated rows, pull-downs).
c. Stabilization exercises—see section VIII.C.7 above.
d. Sample exercises include shrugs, overhead press, lat pull-down, horizontal seated row, upright row with variations, and use of resistive tools.

Group Three—Shoulders: Deltoids/Rotator Cuff

a. Use one hand to support the torso in the bent-over alignment position (e.g., rows, reverse flys). As weight and growth of the uterus progresses, it may be difficult to maintain torso stabilization in a non-supported hip flexed position (e.g., reverse flys).

b. After the first trimester, perform push-ups in a standing position against a wall.

c. To strengthen the rotator cuff, AFAA recommends external rotation with a light weight or strap. In a standing, side-lying, or seated position with the elbow remaining at the side, take the strap or a light weight through a full range of motion.

d. Stabilization exercises—see section VIII.C.7 above.

e. Sample exercises include raises, overhead presses, shoulder cuff rotations with variations, and use of resistive tools.

Group Four—Arms: Biceps/Triceps

a. In a standing position, cue participants to maintain neutral pelvic alignment when performing overhead exercises and kickbacks.

b. Supporting body weight on the wrists may aggravate pregnant women with carpal tunnel syndrome.

c. Sample exercises include curls, overhead exercises, kickbacks, and dips.

Group Five—Hips: Abductors/Adductors

a. Side-lying position—abduction above 45° or shoulder height in this position may strain both the lower back and/or round ligaments.

   1) In this position, adduction exercises, which require the upper leg to cross over the working leg, may be difficult because of the size of the uterus. Resting the upper leg on one or two pillows or a step will reduce stress on the pelvis and maintain better alignment.

   2) In this position, it is recommended that the head rest on the extended arm. Supporting the upper body on the elbows may cause stress to the shoulders.

b. All-fours position—see section VIII.C.5. above.

c. Sample exercises include side-lying leg lifts, ball squeezes, and standing hip abduction.

Group Six—Buttocks: Gluteus Maximus

a. Side-lying position—alternately contract and release gluteal muscles.

b. All-fours positions—observe considerations listed above for exercises performed on all fours (see section VIII.C.7 above).

   1) With the leg bent at the knee, perform hip lifts, pushing one heel toward the ceiling while gluteus muscles contract.

   2) To work one leg behind the body at hip level, bend or curl the lower leg, bringing the heel toward the buttocks, short level. Extend and repeat. If the hip flexors are tight or the participant suffers from round ligament syndrome, full extension of the hip with the leg in a long lever behind the body to hip height may be difficult. Therefore, use short-lever range of motion.

   3) Participants have the option of placing weight on their elbows versus their hands in the all-fours position, especially if carpel tunnel conditions exist. Placing their elbows on a step or chair may be more supportive than placing them on the floor to reduce stress to the torso and pelvic floor.

c. Standing—gluteus muscles are worked as described above by pushing the heel away from the body, keeping the knee bent and buttocks contracted. Due to increasing lordosis, proper alignment becomes more difficult as pregnancy progresses.

d. Avoid supine and prone positions after 20 weeks of gestation.

e. Stabilization exercises—see section VIII.C.7 above.

f. Sample exercises include rear leg lifts, reverse lunges, and wall slides.

Group Seven—Front of the Leg: Quadriceps/Hip Flexors/Tibialis Anterior

a. In a standing position, maintain neutral pelvic alignment with knees aligned over toes.

b. Lunges in a stationary position are appropriate, if executed correctly. Avoid lunges performed by walking forward alternating feet after the first 20 weeks of gestation. Due to instability caused by displaced center of gravity, this variation of lunges may stress knee ligaments, put pressure on the pelvic floor muscles, as well as challenge the pregnant exerciser's balance.

c. Avoid deep-knee bends due to potential stress to knee ligaments.

   d. The traditional weight lifter's squat may be too stressful after the first trimester due to difficulty of maintaining correct torso alignment.

   e. AFAA recommends demonstrating for participants the pregnant squat for women to do at home. This will prepare the legs and pelvic floor for labor and delivery. Movement should be slow and controlled with the availability of holding onto a stationary support structure (e.g., ballet barre) throughout the squat movement. Slowly move into the position, stay as long as it is comfortable, and use legs, buttocks, and stabilized torso, as well as assistance from stationary support structure to push back to a standing position.

   f. As an alternative to the supine position, place a pillow behind the lower back and use the hands to support the upper body. Create a semi-reclining position, with neutral pelvic alignment maintained.

   g. Stabilization exercises (e.g., wall sit) may be performed. However, cue participants to breathe properly to avoid the Valsalva maneuver.

   h. Sample exercises include squats, lunges, leg extensions, knee extensions, and pliés with variations and tools.

Group Eight—Back of the Leg: Hamstrings/Gastrocnemius/ Soleus

   a. Participants may want to use a ballet barre or wall for balance.
   b. Avoid supine and prone positions after 20 weeks of gestation.
   c. Stabilization exercises—see section VIII.C.7 above.
   d. Sample exercises include hamstring curls, heel raises, rear leg lifts, and reverse lunges with variations and tools.
   e. Calf stretches are more important than strength exercises in order to prevent leg cramps.

Group Nine—Front of the Torso: Rectus Abdominis/Obliques/ Transverse Abdominis

   a. Perform abdominal curls slowly at half-time tempo of music.
   b. Avoid fast oblique exercises that may strain round ligaments.
   c. As the uterus enlarges, the degree to which the head, neck, and shoulders are lifted will decrease.
   d. Performing curl-ups with feet elevated becomes increasingly difficult as pregnancy progress. With the belly in the way, range of motion will become restricted.
   e. When performing pelvic tilts in the all-fours position, concentrate on the abdominal muscles instead of the buttocks to tilt the pelvis. If the all-fours position (hands and knees or elbows

and knees) is not comfortable, use incline, sitting, side-lying, or standing positions.

    f.   Omit exercising in a supine position after 20 weeks of gestation.

    g.   Stabilization exercises—see section VIII.C.7 above.

Group Ten—Back of the Torso: Erector Spinae

    a.   The ability to correct and stabilize with the abdominal muscles in order to effectively perform lower back strengthening exercises (using the erector spinae as a primary mover for spinal extension) is difficult during pregnancy. However, indirect strengthening through torso stabilization exercises is considered appropriate during pregnancy, provided participants can execute the exercises correctly.

    b.   Sample exercises in an all-fours position include alternate leg lifts or lifting opposite arm and leg.

    c.   Stabilization exercises—see section VIII.C.7 above.

    d.   No exercises should be performed in the prone position after 13 weeks of gestation, or sooner depending on fetal growth.

IX. Flexibility Training

A. Definition, Purpose, and Duration
See AFAA's *Basic Exercise Standards and Guidelines*, section VIII.1.

B. Methods
See AFAA's *Basic Exercise Standards and Guidelines*, section VIII.2.

C. Special Considerations for Pregnancy

1. Perform static stretches with slow, controlled movements and transitions.

2. Intensity—avoid stretching to maximum muscle length.

3. Stretching on the floor allows for the greatest stability and balance.

4. Observe guidelines regarding standing forward spinal flexion (see section VI.D.1 above). Forward spinal flexion in a sitting position will become increasingly difficult as the uterus expands.

5. Avoid supine position after 20 gestational weeks.

X. Final Class Segment

A. Definition, Purpose, and Duration
See AFAA's *Basic Exercise Standards and Guidelines*, section VIII.F.1.

B. Methods
See AFAA's *Basic Exercise Standards and Guidelines*, section VIII.F.2.

C. Special Considerations for Pregnancy

1. Heart rate should have returned to a normal level. Participants should be at the lower end of perceived exertion.

2. Elevated heart rate may indicate that the participant was exercising at too high of an intensity.

3. If heart rate remains elevated for prolonged periods after cool-down, participants should consult their physician.

4. Contract the muscles in both legs. Starting with the right leg, gradually release all the tension in the toes, ankle, calf, knee, and on up the leg, through the thigh to the hip. Contraction of muscles in the left leg should be maintained, thus teaching participants how to isolate specific muscles.

5. Deep slow breathing should accompany relaxation.

6. Vary contraction/relaxation exercises to teach awareness of tension in the major muscle groups of the upper and lower body, allowing individuals to feel the difference between a relaxed or tensed muscle.

7. Verbally instruct use of imagery to aid in the relaxation process. Ask participants to imagine their bodies being supported by a cloud or all of their joints being made of Jell-O.

8. Always use a soft, near monotone voice when instructing relaxation. It may be useful to dim the lights. Soothing "mood" music, such as the sound of waves or wind, will help relaxation.

9. Types of Relaxation Appropriate for Prenatal Classes
    a. Progressive relaxation focuses on the sensation of tensing and relaxing each muscle.
        1) Move from head to toe or vice versa.
        2) Inhale as you tense, exhale as you relax.
    b. Neuromuscular dissociation selectively tenses some muscles while relaxing others simultaneously.
    c. Autogenic training involves suggestions to influence mental control of neuromuscular and autonomic systems.
        1) Uses words like heavy, warm, melting.
    d. Meditation—concentration on a focal point and breathing patterns to actively focus attention away from discomfort and decrease perception of it.
        1) Om meditation—has several meanings: sound of all sounds, sound of the universe, sound of creation, beginning of life. Has four parts: *ah/oh/mmm/silence. Inhale deeply; on the exhalation begin chanting the om. Pause, repeat.*

   2) Palming meditation—place palms of the hands together, rub quickly, to create heat. Then place over the eyes relaxing fingers; concentrate on relaxing the eye area; remain here and focus on your breath.

   3) Mindfulness meditation—breathe deeply with silent inhalation and exhalation.

e. Visual and guided imagery teaches techniques to visualize pleasurable experiences after reaching a relaxed state.

   1) Positive images for the birth experience and relaxed, peaceful settings

f. Touch relaxation increases other types of sensory input to stimulate large efferent nerve receptors on skin to decrease perception of pain.

   1) An effective way to express support and encouragement

   2) Locates areas of tension and increases ability to consciously relax

h. Yoga—regulated breathing techniques or pranayama (science of breath) is essential for pregnancy, birth, and postpartum. Prana is your life force energy. Practice Ujjai and Anuloma Viloma regularly, as follows.

   1) Ujjai (sounding breath)—sit in a comfortable position; draw the breath in slowly through the nose; fill the abdomen and lungs; keeping the mouth shut, contract the throat slightly to make a soft hissing sound as you exhale; empty lungs completely; allow the breath to be long and slow.

   2) Anuloma Viloma (alternate nostril breath)—sit in a comfortable position; inhale and exhale; close right nostril with thumb; inhale through left nostril; close both nostrils and hold breath; lift thumb and exhale; repeat other side.

4

STANDARDS and GUIDELINES for
Youth Fitness

Introduction

Physical activity is generally considered to be an important factor in the growth and development of children and adolescents. There is a great deal of knowledge which has been generated regarding the effects of exercise on performance and health capacities in children as well as adults. And, research supports the theory that activity habits established early in life continue into adulthood. Schools have historically provided structured physical education programming for our youth. Unfortunately, over the past decade many public schools began eliminating physical education from their curriculums due to financial constraints. However, with the rise in childhood obesity, schools may rethink the value of physical activity and begin to establish it as a priority. Fitness professionals may find a niche in assisting their local schools and communities to recreate physical activity programs; making them fun and rewarding, while improving the health of children around the world.

The information contained in these guidelines reflects the latest research on fitness programming for children and adolescents. Readers are encouraged, however, to keep abreast of new findings and developments in youth fitness because the field of pediatric exercise science continues to evolve. The primary focus of quality youth fitness programming is to instill an intrinsic desire for lifelong activity.

The Youth Fitness Standards and Guidelines apply to an average child and/or adolescent without known physiological or medical conditions that would in any way restrict their ability to participate in any form of physical activity. These standards and guidelines are designed to be used in conjunction with AFAA's *Basic Exercise Standards and Guidelines*.

I. Basic Principles, Definitions, and Recommendations

A. Definitions

1. **Youth Fitness Programs**

   Youth fitness programs offer types of exercise which enhance the following components of fitness: (a) flexibility, (b) muscular strength and endurance, (c) agility, (d) balance, (e) coordination, (f) cardiovascular endurance, and (g) body composition. Movement patterns which help to develop motor skills and cognitive function are also encouraged. Youth fitness does not necessarily imply that the activities are performed at a low intensity, as the intensity may vary according to age group and ability of each child. In addition, activity level depends on exercise selection, sequencing, and movement patterns.

2. **Growth**

   Growth refers to changes in size, measured by weight and stature (height).

   a. Stages of postnatal growth:

      1) Infancy—the first year of life characterized by rapid growth of most bodily systems.

      2) Early childhood—1 to 5 years of age; a stage of rapid growth of trunk, lower extremities, and large muscle groups.

      3) Middle childhood—6 to 10 years of age; a period of relatively steady progress in growth and maturation of all bodily functions.

      4) Prepubescent—children who have not developed secondary sex characteristics. Usually up to 11 years of age in girls and 13 years of age in boys.

      5) Adolescence—12 to 18 years of age in girls and 14 to 18 years of age in boys; a period during which most bodily systems become mature in both structure and function. Structurally, adolescence begins with an acceleration in the rate of growth (commonly known as a "growth spurt"). Functionally, it is viewed as sexual maturation, beginning with an initial development of secondary sex characteristics and terminating with the attainment of mature reproductive function.

   b. Stature

      Stature, or height, is the most obvious difference between children and adults. Height is a consideration when: (a) expecting children to cover distance in a specified time (children take 2–3 times more steps than adults to cover the same distance), and (b) changing levels, such as stepping up and down utilizing a bench or platform (platform height should be in proportion to the child's leg length and physical ability).

3. **Maturation**

   Maturation refers to the process of growth and development which leads to achievement of adult characteristics. Maturation varies considerably among individuals and/or biological systems at any given age.

B. Importance of Physical Fitness and Movement

The promotion of physical activity in early and late childhood may be important in developing lifelong habits that may forestall future chronic illness, such as high blood pressure, elevated blood serum cholesterol, increased body fat, and heart disease. Early participation in physical activity has also demonstrated an increase in performance levels of fitness and motor skills. Numerous studies have supported the premise that important health and performance characteristics can be improved in children as a result of exercise.

The rationale for starting children on an exercise program at an early age includes, but is not limited to: (a) improved ability to meet the demands of daily physical activities, (b) improved results in physical performance tests, (c) improved motor skills, (d) reduced injuries, and (e) fewer chronic health conditions and a lower risk for developing chronic health problems than sedentary children. In addition, physical activity has demonstrated development of: (a) self-esteem, (b) self-confidence, (c) responsibility, (d) social skills, (e) kinesthetic and spatial awareness, and (f) freedom of expression. Based on these important findings, children of all ages should be encouraged to be more physically active on a daily basis.

C. When Children Should Start Exercising

Guidelines for fitness and sports participation for preschool children younger than 5 years of age must be based on careful consideration of the physical fitness needs as well as the unique developmental requirements and limitations of this age group. Therefore, the following recommendations are suggested for **fitness programs for children younger than 5 years of age.**

1. All preschool children should participate in physical activity appropriate for their developmental level and physical health.

2. Goals for accelerating motor development to maximize later sports ability are inappropriate and futile.

3. Free play is preferable to structured exercise sessions in this age group.

4. Sports and fitness programs should be supervised by adults knowledgeable about the specific needs and limitations of preschool children.

5. Parents should serve as role models for children. Physical activities that parents can perform with young children should be encouraged.

D. Physical Ability vs. Chronological Age

1. First Skills Phase or Fundamental Movement Stage: 2–5 years of age (preschool period): children begin to develop locomotion, stability, and manipulation.

2. Basic Fitness Phase or Mature Stages of Fundamental Movement Phase: 6–8 years of age.

3. Early Team Phase: 8–10 years of age: this is a transitional stage from fundamental movement to sports-related skills.

4. Sports Related Phase: 10–14 years of age: children select specific sports or movement skills in which they wish to become proficient.

5. Specialized Movement Stage: 14–17 years of age: a stage that represents the final choice of activities a child may tend to pursue in adulthood.

E. Instructor Qualifications

Instructors who are well-versed in child development and exercise and fitness concepts will have the leading edge when working with youth. They should maintain current instructor certification(s), CPR/AED, and advanced first-aid. Certain states may require low-level FBI clearance and tuberculosis (TB) testing of instructors working with children, particularly for those working within the public school system. It is suggested that all fitness instructors inquire about such state regulations before beginning a youth fitness program.

F. Role of Instructor

1. Instructors must be objective and flexible when teaching multiple age groups in order to offer effective and challenging programs.

2. Instructors must feel comfortable in their ability to work with children, and be able to present fitness and play activities in a creative and innovative manner.

3. Instructors are often most successful when they are able to: (a) think like a child, (b) motivate and positively reinforce, (c) serve as healthy and fit role models, (d) set realistic goals, (e) emphasize that all participants are winners, and (f) provide a safe environment.

4. Instructors are encouraged to design a program that allows the children involved to participate in age-specific physical activity, encouraging personal best, in a structured, fun, and non-competitive atmosphere.

G. Environmental Safety

To help ensure the safety of young fitness program participants, instructors are encouraged to follow the guidelines below.

1. Children should be supervised at all times by the instructor or another responsible adult.
2. When working with very young children:
   a. windows and storage cabinets should be locked when possible to prevent accidents.
   b. electrical outlets should be covered.
3. Floor and/or walls should be padded or, if not, use gym mats for specific activities.
4. Lighting should be bright.
5. The exercise room should be free of sharp or obstructive objects.
6. All equipment, when not in use, should be properly stored.
7. Water sources or fountains should be readily available.

H. Equipment

1. Equipment for children should be designed for the specific age group, according to size, material, weight, height, and safety regulations.
2. Equipment for children should be fun, safe, and quick and easy to store.
3. Young children love to use such props as balls, balloons, hula hoops, feathers, hats, gloves, and various costumes. Use your imagination. You might even ask the children what they enjoy playing with.
4. Creating homemade equipment (e.g., bean bags made from scraps of material filled with rice or beans, and weights made from plastic bottles filled with water or sand) can be fun, creative, and interactive projects.

I. Music

1. Determine themes and use a variety of tunes.
2. Create an atmosphere through music selection.
3. Choose catchy melodies specific to certain age groups.
4. Utilize rhythms that are easy to move to.
5. Allow children to choose their favorite tunes.

II. Youth Fitness Endurance Training Principles and Guidelines (5 Years of Age Through Adolescence)

Studies have demonstrated that children physiologically adapt to endurance training. As with all forms of cardiorespiratory training, the response in children varies. Children should participate in a variety of age-appropriate physical activities designed to achieve optimal health, wellness, fitness, and performance benefits (ACSM, 2010; NASPE, 2004).

A. Frequency

In general, children and adolescents should participate in physical activity a minimum of 3–4 days per week and preferably daily (ACSM 2010; USDHHS, 2008; NASPE, 2004).

B. Duration

The attention span and physical capacity of children vary depending on their age and developmental stage. Therefore, it is important for the instructor to establish a specific amount of time appropriate for the chronological age and developmental level of his/her participants. For youth, the duration of activity may be more beneficial than the intensity due to the various developmental stages of maturation. A longer, less intense activity program may allow for a greater attention span with less physiological stress and provide positive health and social benefits. Therefore, children and adolescents should participate in several bouts of physical activity lasting 15 minutes or more each day to accumulate at least 60 minutes, and up to several hours, of age appropriate physical activity (ACSM 2010; USDHHS, 2008; NASPE, 2004).

C. Intensity

As previously mentioned under duration, it is important for the instructor to establish an intensity level appropriate for the chronological age and developmental level of his/her participants. To provide an aerobic training effect, an activity should provide sufficient progressive overload to maintain a training heart rate. The exercise intensity should start out low and progress gradually, and should be of either moderate or vigorous intensity. Moderate intensity is defined by the American College of Sports Medicine as physical activity that noticeably increases breathing, sweating, and heart rate while vigorous intensity is defined as physical activity that substantially increases breathing, sweating, and heart rate. It is recommended to use the RPE scale when monitoring heart rate in children. It is suggested that the RPE scale be modified for youth fitness programs so that it is easier to understand (Table 4.1.). For a group cardio fitness class, exercise selection, elevated movement, movement patterns and sequencing, speed and lever length are important in regulating the exercise intensity.

Table 4.1.

MODIFIED BORG SCALE FOR CHILDREN RATING OF PERCEIVED EXERTION SCALE FOR CHILDREN Reprinted with permission from Scott Roberts.		
INTENSITY	**EXPLANATION**	**VISUAL EXAMPLE**
0-rest	How you feel when you are sitting and resting.	Child sitting in a chair or watching TV.
1-easy	How you feel when you are walking to school or doing chores around the house.	Child walking to school; no sweat.
2-pretty hard	How you feel when you are playing.	Child playing and just starting to sweat.
3-harder	How you feel when you are playing sports, playing hard on the playground, or working hard.	Child playing sports and sweating.
4-hard	How you feel when you are running hard.	Child running hard and sweating profusely.
5-very hard, maximal	The hardest you have ever worked or exercised in your life.	Child running and ready to collapse at the finish line of a race.

1. **Activity Selection**
   Children can achieve health benefits when participating in a variety of activities, such as play, games, sports, work, transportation, recreation, physical education, or planned exercise, in the context of family, school, and community activites.

2. **Exercise Selection**
   The variety of movements used and choice of exercise appropriate for the child's fitness level will be a determining factor in raising or lowering exercise intensity, as well as maintaining a consistent intensity level throughout the cardio or aerobic portion of the class. To determine the appropriate activities for a beginner, the instructor should design an activity questionnaire (see Appendix A of this chapter).

3. **Speed of Movement**
   (See AFAA's *Basic Exercise Standards and Guidelines*, section V.B.10.)
   The younger and less developed a child is, the slower his/her response time will be. Response time is divided into two components: (a) reaction time, and (b) movement time. The instructor

should be concerned with total response time in young children, making sure that demonstration of the desired movement pattern(s) is performed at a speed at which a young child can interpret and then perform. Total response time will improve as one develops physically and chronologically up to 20 years of age.

Length of arms and legs should also be considered when performing rhythmic limbering exercises. Children who have shorter limbs will move from side to center sooner than those with longer limbs. Therefore, variations in movement patterns and choreography should be applied according to the size of the participants and their physical abilities.

4. **Muscle Strengthening**
   (See AFAA's *Basic Exercise Standards and Guidelines*, section VIII.D.)

   Muscular strengthening can be achieved in a youth fitness class without the use of added weight by the same methods utilized in traditional adult aerobic and body conditioning classes and with non-weighted floorwork. Factors to control include body position, muscle isolation, range of motion, and repetitions.

5. **Posture and Alignment**
   Refer to AFAA's *Basic Exercise Standards and Guidelines*, sections VI.C and VIII.D, as well as alignment for specific body positions for muscle strengthening.

III. Class Format

Each program should be geared to a specific age group and defined by the cognitive, biomechanical, and physiological capabilities of participants at each age level. Children between 2–5 years of age and 6–8 years of age respond more to programs emphasizing movement and play than specific fitness goals.

Individuals between 9 years of age and adulthood should participate in programs that emphasize the development of physical fitness components, such as cardiovascular endurance, muscular strength and endurance, flexibility, balance, agility, and coordination.

Design a program that will motivate children of all ages to develop positive, healthy, lifelong fitness habits.

A. Sequence

Class sequence for the older child (16–18 years of age) who is participating in aerobic dance exercise will be the same as adult programming. (See AFAA's *Basic Exercise Standards and Guidelines*, sections VII and VIII.)

1. **Pre-class Instruction and Announcements**
   a. Younger children have shorter attention spans than older children. Therefore, the time allotted for pre-class instruction should be adjusted according to the age and maturity level of the participants.
   b. From middle childhood to adolescence, teach how to take heart rate and the importance of monitoring heart rate during an exercise program.
   c. Periodically reinforce proper breathing techniques and body alignment for all ages.
   d. Include terminology and "real-life" examples that children are familiar with.

2. **Warm-up**
   It is important to establish a habit of warming up the body prior to engaging in any strenuous activity. Therefore, children should be well-versed on the purpose of a warm-up. For the younger child whose attention span is short, a warm-up that is creative and fun is encouraged.

3. **Cardio (Aerobic) Session**
   Youth fitness aerobics programming for cardiorespiratory conditioning may vary according to chronological age and maturity level of participants (see AFAA's *Basic Exercise Standards and Guidelines*, section VIII.C.). Keep in mind that modifications may need to be made in: (a) the sequencing, speed, and difficulty of movements; (b) the height of steps or benches; and (c) the type and size of playful props used with children.

4. **Post-aerobic Cool-down**
   The purpose of the cool-down is to prevent blood from pooling in the lower extremities following aerobic exercise. Light activities during the cool-down may also help prevent muscle soreness.

5. **Floorwork**
   Exercises from the following groups may be performed in order of preference: (a) legs, (b) buttocks, (c) hips, (d) abdominals, and (e) lower back (see AFAA's *Basic Exercise Standards and Guidelines*, section VIII.D.2–4). The number of repetitions and intensity of movements should be reduced for youth fitness classes.

6. **Cool-down Static Stretches**
   The purpose of the final cool-down static stretch is to increase the flexibility within the joints and return the body to a normal, relaxed state. (See AFAA's *Basic Exercise Standards and Guidelines*, section VIII.E.)

B. Types of Movement

1. 2–5 Years of Age

a. Focus on developing body awareness and responding to movement stimuli using music, sounds, and equipment to help develop lateral movement skills, body control, balance, eye-hand coordination, and body image.

b. To develop spatial awareness, visual perception, and fundamental motor skills (gross motor and locomotive movements), utilize activities such as climbing over, under, in, and out; jumping; catching; falling; running; hopping; and skipping. Many of these activities may be incorporated into fun obstacle courses with colorful equipment and creative play set to music. Cognitive learning may be developed through the use of specific body parts, shapes, and colors.

c. Fantasy or make believe movement adventures encourage children to explore a wide range of movement patterns in a continuous, creative, and fun manner.

d. Children move with intermittent bursts of energy. Therefore, classes should be well supervised, yet loosely structured and designed to follow children's natural movement patterns.

e. Sample class format

Class Length:	20–40 minutes
Pre-class Instruction: (including health/fitness tips)	3–5 minutes
Warm-up:	3–5 minutes
Activity Session:	15–20 minutes
Cool–down:	3–5 minutes
Closure (award system):	3–5 minutes

(See section X.B of this chapter.)

2. 6–8 Years of Age

a. Focus on increased body awareness, rhythm and coordination, music memory, further development of motor skills, and eye-hand coordination. A circuit format is ideal for this age group since attention span is short. The circuit should include a variety of different exercise stations to challenge the individual, help increase awareness and isolate different body parts.

b. Group activities which include multi-impact movement combinations to help develop rhythm and muscle memory as well as group cooperative games are encouraged. This age group can also benefit from more complex obstacle courses which incorporate the use of large muscles, locomotive skills, visual perception, spatial awareness, and cognitive and motor functions.

c. Introduce participants to basic sports skills.

d. Introduce kid's step and slide programs.

e. Sample class format

Class Length:	45–60 minutes
Pre-class Instruction:	5 minutes
(including health/fitness tips)	
Warm-up:	5–10 minutes
Activity Session:	25–30 minutes
Cool-down:	5–10 minutes
Closure (award system):	5 minutes

3. **9–11 Years of Age**

a. Design a program that will increase physical skills (e.g., a circuit which combines movement sequences, cardiovascular conditioning, muscle strength and endurance, flexibility, agility, and balance).

b. Cooperative games may be incorporated to enhance social skills and group play (sportsmanship).

c. Introduce fun, creative, low-impact aerobic dance exercise. Instructor may also choose to introduce children to kid's step and slide programs.

d. Introduce strength training. Teach proper technique and form using natural resistance and light weights (1/2–1 lb).

e. Sample class format

Class Length:	45–60 minutes
Pre-class Instruction:	5 minutes
(including health/fitness tips)	
Warm-up:	5–10 minutes
Aerobic Conditioning:	20 minutes
Post-aerobic Cool-down:	5 minutes
Strengthening:	10–15 minutes
Final Cool-down:	3–5 minutes

4. **12–15 Years of Age**

a. Focus on exercises that stress the components of physical fitness, such as cardiovascular endurance, muscular strength and endurance, flexibility, agility, and balance.

b. The use of circuits and advanced obstacle courses are appropriate.

    c.   All related sports, both individual and team, are of particular interest to this age group. Instructors may focus on developing sports skills.

    d.   Introduce more challenging movement patterns for low-impact aerobic dance.

    e.   Continue in strength training (see section VIII of this chapter).

    f.   Gradually increase the intensity and duration of the aerobic portion of class until minimum adult standards are met. (See AFAA's *Basic Exercise Standards and Guidelines*, section VIII.C.)

    g.   Keep participants moving to burn calories.

5. 16–18 Years of Age

    a.   Instructors may choose to focus on advanced skills and play strategies for individual and team athletic sports.

    b.   Instruction in aerobic dance exercise, funk, step, and slide (if equipment is available) may be incorporated in a program designed for this age group.

    c.   For class format, see AFAA's *Basic Exercise Standards and Guidelines*, section VII.

IV. Pre-Class Health Screening and Announcements

A. Instructor Checklist

Review points to cover in AFAA's *Basic Exercise Standards and Guidelines*, sections IV–VI. Because children are not able to give legal consent, parents must sign a permission or consent form before children should be allowed to participate in youth fitness classes. Instructors should take the following steps before children are allowed to exercise.

1. Verify that medical clearance has been obtained.

2. Determine the appropriate level of participation.

3. Ensure appropriate shoes are being worn.

4. Instruct the child on how to breathe properly during exercise.

5. Give an aerobic class orientation. An instructor may wish to include a description of and directions for the day's activities, a special healthy thought in regard to aerobic fitness, the reward for the day if one is being given, and so forth.

6. Determine and explain the training heart rate and perceived exertion levels.

7. Review safety procedures.

B. Youth Fitness Orientation

Familiarize youth participants with important body alignment cues for maintaining proper positioning and receiving optimal fitness benefits from their workout. You may choose to repeat these cues often throughout the program. Review the following important points, using demonstrations if necessary.

1. Complete all movements through the full range of motion.
2. Control the speed of movements.
3. Use arms, legs, and feet during combinations and movement patterns to maintain workout intensity.

V. Warm-Up (Middle Childhood Through Adolescence)

A. Purpose

To prepare the body for vigorous exercise and reduce the risk of injury.

B. Time

Class should always begin with a 5–10 minute warm-up, including exercises specific to muscles that will be utilized during the workout. Some studies have shown that children do not need as lengthy a warm-up as adults.

C. Specific Warm-Up Guidelines

The guidelines for warm-up sequence, muscle groups, rhythmic limbering exercises, and special do's and don'ts, as described in AFAA's *Basic Exercise Standards and Guidelines*, section VIII.B, should be followed for a youth fitness class.

VI. Cardiorespiratory Conditioning Without Weights (Middle Childhood Through Adolescence)

A. Purpose

To train the cardiovascular and respiratory systems to exchange and deliver oxygen quickly and efficiently to each part of the body being exercised.

1. Special Concerns
   a. Aerobic capacity—a prepubescent child's maximum capacity for oxygen utilization (VO_{2max}) averages 1 liter per minute compared to 3 liters per minute for a 21-year-old. A 7-year-old boy has approximately ¼ the muscle mass of an adult male. This difference in size is the primary reason for the variance in aerobic capacity between adults and children. Due to this reduced work capacity in children, adult norms should be adjusted accordingly for aerobic activities when programming youth fitness.

b. Children's capacity for anaerobic exercise is also dramatically reduced due to size, growth, and development. Therefore, fatigue may occur sooner than expected during high-intensity activities. Intersperse anaerobic activities with breaks to enable the children to rest and hydrate.

c. Children have increased ventilatory rates due to smaller lungs.

B. Time

20–45 minutes, not including warm-up or post-aerobic cool-down.

C. Sequence

Start slowly, gradually increasing the intensity and range of motion of your movements until such time when a steady-state has been achieved, approximately 3–5 minutes after the cardio or aerobic portion has begun.

Heart rate (HR) in youth fitness programs should be maintained in the 55–80% range of estimated maximum heart rate. Generally, intensity should range from moderate (where there is a noticeable increase in breathing, sweating, and HR) to vigorous (substantial increases in breathing, sweating, and HR). The use of the RPE scale is the preferred method for monitoring exercise intensity in children and adolescents. HR may be elevated or decreased by regulating the intensity of the exercises. Factors affecting intensity can be found in section II.C. of this chapter.

VII. Post-Aerobic Cool-Down (Middle Childhood Through Adolescence)

A. Purpose

To provide a transition period between vigorous aerobic work and less taxing exercise, thus allowing working heart rate to safely return to pre-exercise rate without overstressing cardiorespiratory function (children seem to recover from exercise faster than adults).

B. Time

2–5 minutes

C. Sequence

Rhythmic movement that gradually decreases in speed and range of motion.

D. Method

At the end of the cardiorespiratory segment, AFAA recommends performing 3–5 minutes of lower-intensity rhythmic activity. An appropriately designed cool-down will help participants avoid blood pooling in the extremities as well as aid them in a gradual heart rate recovery Youth fitness instructors may also want to include some upright static stretches for the back, shoulders, and arms, as well as calves, quadriceps, hamstrings, and front of shins to regain the range of motion and flexibility in muscles that have been shortened during the workout.

VIII. Major Muscle Conditioning

See AFAA's *Basic Exercise Standards and Guidelines*, section VIII.D. The number of repetitions may need to be appropriately adjusted for different age groups and various fitness levels. Begin muscle strengthening programs with slow, progressive stages, starting with 6–8 repetitions and gradually increasing the repetitions as children become more proficient and ready for a challenge. The instructor's role is to try to avoid risk of injury to his/her young, developing participants.

IX. Resistance Training Guidelines and Recommendations

A. Introduction and Recommendations

The issue of children lifting weights was not widely accepted until recently. Early investigators led many to believe that strength gains were not even possible in prepubescent children, and strength training could cause irreversible injury to the developing growth plates in bones. However, new research has encouraged resistance training in children for health benefits. Furthermore, the safety and efficacy of resistance training programs for prepubescent children have been well documented. In addition to improvements in muscular strength, other fitness and performance related effects of resistance training include: (a) increased flexibility, (b) improved physical performance, (c) improved body composition, (d) improved cardiorespiratory fitness, (e) reduced serum lipids, and (f) reduced blood pressure. With further research, additional benefits may be realized.

1. **Resistance Training**
   Children should be encouraged to participate in a variety of activities that involve repetitive movements against an opposing force including their own body weight.

2. **Free Weight Training**
   Proper lifting techniques and safety are the two most important factors to consider. Start with small 1/2 to 1-pound dumbbells. Perform a variety of upper and lower body exercises.

3. **Weight Training Machines**
   With the exception of several companies which manufacture weight training equipment specifically for children, most exercise equipment is designed for adults. If children cannot be properly fitted for the machines, do not use them.

4. **Manual Resistance Training**

   With manual resistance training, resistance is provided by a partner. Children take turns applying resistance during different movements. For example, to perform hip abduction, one child lies on the ground while the other child applies resistance to the leg performing the exercise. Caution should be taken while performing partner resistant or stretching exercises. Make sure the children are at a psychological maturity level to understand the importance of performing correct technique and potential risk for injury while performing manual resistance training (10 years of age and up).

5. **Isometric Training**

   Isometric training occurs when muscles are contracted, but do not change in length. For example, to perform standing upright lateral arm raises, one child tries to raise his/her arms up and out to the sides while the other child applies the resistant force at the upper arms preventing arms from moving upward (partner work). Isometric exercises can also be done individually.

6. **Tubing Exercises**

   Exercise tubing can be purchased or made from scratch in different levels of resistance. All resistance exercises should be performed in a slow, steady, sustained manner. Use a specific count during the initial movement, the hold phase, and then return to the resting phase.

7. **Additional Programs**

   To perform pulling activities, tie a rope to a wall and have the children pull themselves toward the wall while sitting on a piece of carpet, or they may pull weighted sandbags toward themselves. Pushing activities include push-ups and throwing a medicine ball. For hanging activities, the child may hang from a bar, swing, or slowly release from an assisted pull-up (eccentric work).

8. **Strengthening Without the Use of Weights**

   If strengthening exercises without weights are to be included for the upper body (e.g., arms, chest, shoulders, back and/or legs, buttocks, abdominals), see AFAA's *Basic Exercise Standards and Guidelines*, section VIII.D.

B. Specific Guidelines

Studies in the 1970s and 1980s had shown that individuals between 10 and 19 years of age were particularly prone to injury during strength training. Therefore, resistance training was not recommended for children and adolescents. However, many of the reported injuries were actually caused by inappropriate training techniques, excessive load-ing, poorly designed equipment, ready access to the equipment, or lack of qualified adult supervision (NSCA, 2009; Kraemer & Fleck, 1993). When designing resistance training programs, it is important to se-lect exercises that are appropriate for a child's body size, fitness level, and exercise technique experience. Also, the choice of exercises should promote muscle balance across joints and between opposing muscle groups (e.g., biceps and triceps). Weight machines (both child-size and adult-size) as well as free weights, elastic bands, medicine balls, and body weight exercises have been used by children and adolescents in clinical- and school-based fitness programs (NSCA, 2009).

The following precautions should be taken with children when they participate in a strength training program.

- Children should be at such a level of emotional and physical matu-rity that they can understand and follow specific rules and instruc-tional procedures.
- Exercises in a group situation should be fun and non-competitive. Competition is acceptable on an individual level when a child is seeking self-improvement, and can be rewarded by his/her own personal drive, self-esteem, and goal setting.
- Emphasize higher repetitions (12–16), more sets (2–4), and less weight. Lifting heavier weights depends on the child's individual maturation level and training experience.
- Lifting maximal, or near-maximal, resistance (less than 6 reps) is not recommended during a child's developmental years. Injuries may occur related to the long bones and the back.
- Supervision by competent instructors is very important.
- The instructor should teach proper warm-up and stretching tech-niques prior to lifting weights.
- Children and adolescents should learn to perform a variety of cal-isthenic and strength training exercises.
- Children should learn the purpose of performing each exercise and how to combine them into a logical sequence or progression.
- Strength training should be part of a complete fitness program which includes cardiovascular fitness, flexibility, and a well-bal-anced diet.
- Encourage children to keep track of their progress through the use of logs, charts, creative maps, and so forth.

The following "Basic Guidelines for Resistance Exercise Progression in Children" was written by William J. Kraemer, Ph.D. and Steven J. Fleck, Ph.D., authors of *Strength Training for Young Athletes*.

- Age 7 or Younger—Introduce child to basic exercises with little or no weight. Develop the concept of a training session. Teach exercise techniques, progressing from body weight calisthenics to partner exercises and lightly resisted exercises. Deep volume (a measure of the total work—sets x repetitions x resistance for a given exercises, training session or training period) low.

- Ages 8–10—Gradually increase the number of exercises. Practice technique in all lifts. Start gradual progressive loading of exercises (see AFAA's *Standards and Guidelines for Group Resistance Training [GRT]*). Keep exercises simple. Gradually increase volume. Carefully monitor toleration to the exercises stress.

- Ages 11–13—Teach all basic exercise techniques. Continue progressive loading of each exercise, emphasizing techniques. Introduce more advanced exercises with little or no resistance.

- Ages 14–15—Progress to more advanced youth programs in resistance exercise. Add sport-specific components, emphasizing exercise techniques and increasing volume.

- Age 16 and Older—Move child to entry-level adult programs after all background knowledge has been mastered and a basic level of training experience has been gained.

NOTE: Gradually introduce a child to a resistance training program by slowly progressing to more advanced levels as exercise toleration, skill, amount of training time, and understanding permit.

In 2009, the National Strength and Conditioning Association (NSCA) released their latest guidelines for youth resistance training. They are as follows.

- Provide qualified instruction and supervision.
- Ensure the exercise environment is safe and free of hazards.
- Start each training session with a 5- to 10-minute dynamic warm-up period.
- Begin with relatively light loads and always focus on the correct exercise technique.
- Perform 1–3 sets of 6–15 repetitions on a variety of upper- and lower-body strength exercises.
- Include specific exercises that strengthen the abdominal and lower back region.
- Focus on symmetrical muscular development and appropriate muscle balance around joints.
- Perform 1–3 sets of 3–6 repetitions on a variety of upper- and lower-body power exercises.

- Sensibly progress the training program depending on needs, goals, and abilities.
- Increase the resistance gradually (5–10%) as strength improves.
- Cool down with less intense calisthenics and static stretching.
- Listen to individual needs and concerns throughout each session.
- Begin resistance training two to three times per week on nonconsecutive days.
- Use individualized workout logs to monitor progress.
- Keep the program fresh and challenging by systematically varying the training program.
- Optimize performance and recovery with healthy nutrition, proper hydration, and adequate sleep.
- Support and encouragement from instructors and parents will help maintain interest.

X. Special Considerations Related to Youth Fitness

A. Growth and Development Issues

1. Activity increases skeletal growth. For example, vigorous activity may affect the bone structure and strength, thus creating more resistance to injury.

2. The growth plates do not fuse until maturity when hardening of the bones occurs (which may not be until 18–20 years of age). Maturation of the skeletal system occurs at different rates in different individuals. There may be a 5-to 6-year difference between chronological age and skeletal maturity.

3. In children, muscular strength develops concurrent with chronological development.

4. Lean body weight is the most important factor in the development of strength and power in children.

5. Many experts profess that physical activity begun and consistently performed in childhood has an impact on the child's body and activity level throughout life.

6. As children mature, their responses to training improve. Both strength and maximal oxygen uptake are strongly related to the proportion of lean body mass in developing children.

7. The degree to which children can improve physiological measures depends on growth and maturation rates and the exercise stimulus during exercise training.

B. Psychological Issues

Unlike adults, young children will not exercise when fatigued for the sake of health, beauty, or fitness. Motivation levels differ between adults, teens, and children. Though extrinsic motivators should not be relied upon too heavily, it may be necessary to provide tangible reinforcers, such as stars, stickers, and certificates to help motivate the younger child. These reinforcers should be linked with praise. With age, tangible reinforcers may be diminished as children become more intrinsically motivated. Keep in mind that people of all ages need praise, recognition, and positive motivational tips from fitness professionals.

C. Medical Issues

1. Asthma

In the United States, approximately 9 million children are affected by asthma. The National Heart, Lung, and Blood Institute recommends that children with asthma exercise when they are feeling well. Start slowly and gradually build into an exercise program. Consult with parents and physician prior to starting any exercise program.

2. Diabetes

It is recommended to encourage children with controlled diabetes to exercise. Participation in regular exercise helps to expend energy, reduce body fat, and improve diabetic control. Instructors should be well versed on diabetes, its symptoms, treatment, and emergency protocol.

3. Obesity

The benefits of regular exercise participation for the obese child is not limited to weight loss. Other benefits of exercise for these children include reduction in blood serum cholesterol and blood pressure and and increase in positive self-image. Lead the obese child through a slow, progressive exercise program to ensure continual participation.

XI. Injury Prevention

A. **Research indicates** children tolerate increases in workloads equal to adults, but modified for height and size.

B. **Physiological factors** influence children while exercising during hot weather. Children have:

1. higher surface area/mass ratios.

2. greater amount of heat transfer between the body and environment.

3. greater metabolic heat production than adults performing the same activity.
4. less sweating capacity than adults.
5. decreased ability to get rid of heat, due to lowered cardiac output and size.

C. Hot Weather Precautions

1. Monitor temperature and humidity, and adjust activities accordingly.
2. Until adaptation occurs, children acclimating to hot temperatures should use a gradual approach to strenuous fitness programs. Instructors should be aware that children tend to have a 20–30% greater energy expenditure than adults during aerobic activities. This coupled with lower sweat rates, lower cardiac output, and greater surface area to mass ratio can impair temperature regulation. Children should drink water frequently and exercise for less than 30 minutes in temperatures over 85° Fahrenheit.
3. Children should be encouraged to drink cool fluids prior to, during, and after activity. Cool water is recommended over other fluids, such as juice, soda, and Gatorade, unless participating in prolonged activities exceeding 1 hour. Avoid fluids with caffeine as these can promote dehydration.
4. Children should wear a lightweight, single layer of absorbent material so sweat evaporation is facilitated.
5. The American Academy of Pediatrics Committee on Sports Medicine has identified children with the following conditions to be at high risk for heat stress problems.
   - Obesity
   - Fevers or sweating syndrome
   - Cystic fibrosis, gastrointestinal infections, diabetes insipidus, diabetes mellitus, chronic heart failure, malnutrition, anorexia nervosa, and mental deficiency

D. Distance Running and Children

The International Athletics Association Federation Medical Committee states the following about distance running and children. "The danger certainly exists that with over-intensive training, separation of the growth plates may occur in the pelvic region, the knee, or the ankle." In fact, the Committee recommends that children under 12 years of age run no more than 1/2 mile in competition.

E. Most Common Childhood Injuries

1. Cuts, bruises, and scrapes
2. Joint sprains
3. Muscular strains
4. Fractures

F. To help ensure against injury during exercise, it is suggested that children:

1. have thorough physical exams before pursuing an exercise program.
2. be cautioned about abruptly increasing the intensity, duration, or frequency of exercise.
3. participate in a warm-up and cool-down.
4. perform flexibility exercises following a brief cardiovascular warm-up.
5. wear proper clothing and footwear.
6. exercise in a safe environment. Be aware of spacing, floor surfaces, lighting, ventilation, foreign objects, and so forth. Program should be well supervised, with children aware of specific rules and regulations.
7. stop exercising if they feel dizzy, lightheaded, nauseous, and/or any pain (see "Danger Signs" in AFAA's *Basic Exercise Standards and Guidelines*).

G. Emergency Protocol

1. **First-aid Technique**
   a. Instructors are encouraged to remain current on immediate first-aid procedures so they are able to deal effectively with emergencies. Be familiar with the "essentials of wound care." They are:
      1) stop the bleeding.
      2) cleanse the wound.
      3) protect the wound.
      4) treat for shock.
   b. Have an emergency game plan so you know who to call, how to call, and what to do in case of serious injury.
   c. Know and practice cardiopulmonary resuscitation (CPR) and automated electronic defibrillator (AED) protocols
   d. Practice RICE—Rest, Ice, Compression, and Elevation

2. **First-aid Materials**

A comprehensive first-aid kit for the treatment of injuries should be easily accessible to instructors. Check to make sure your kit and facility have the following materials.

a. Ice, ice chest, and plastic bags
b. Elastic bandages of varying widths
c. Soap or antiseptic
d. Bandages and gauze
e. Band-Aids
f. Splinting material
g. Sling
h. Clean water
i. Athletic tape
j. Scissors
k. Syrup of Ipecac
l. Smelling salts
m. Rubber gloves
n. Disposable mask for CPR
o. AED

H. Miscellaneous

1. Discipline/Control

   Be consistent in managing discipline and enforcing rules. Younger children who are acting out of control may be asked to:

   a. take a "time-out" (designate a safe and supervised space in the exercise room for "time-outs").
   b. receive pre-established consequences after initial warnings.

2. Encourage parents to participate in their child's fitness program when appropriate. This can reinforce: (a) family togetherness, (b) parent as active role model, and (c) a further involvement in family activities.

3. Competition vs. Cooperation

   a. Cooperative sports and activities help to develop social skills both physically and emotionally (e.g., respect for others, sportsmanship, communication, and team-play).
   b. Competitive sports and activities can promote positive self-esteem and an inner drive to reach one's potential. However, competitive sports and competition in general may not be for everyone and could actually have a negative effect on children who are unprepared physically and/or emotionally for this type of environment.

STANDARDS and GUIDELINES for
Senior Fitness
Part 1: Healthy Sedentary Older Adults

I. Introduction

Regular physical activity proves to be a positive measure for older adults in improving this population's ability to carry out general daily tasks. Experts have shown that exercise is a must at any age, and maintaining a regular exercise program throughout life may lead to longevity and to a better quality of life. The primary goal of any exercise program is to improve or maintain the health of the individual exercise participant. Aside from the obvious health benefits, consistent, progressive exercise has also been shown to be one of the key factors in successful aging.

Many instructors have lacked the knowledge and confidence to provide safe and effective fitness programs for the senior participant. With more research being conducted and a greater confidence level established within the medical profession concerning exercise programming for the elderly, our society is seeing a rise in the need for the development of physical fitness programs for older adults as well as qualified instructors to teach them.

For health care and fitness professionals who are interested in senior fitness, the following questions may be of concern: How much exercise is too much and what types of exercise are contraindicated? AFAA, through the research of many respected individuals in the fields of gerontology, exercise physiology, and fitness instruction, recommends these standards and guidelines for safe and effective exercise for the average healthy, ambulatory older adult participant. Guidelines for the disabled, nonambulatory, and/or institutionalized elderly are addressed in Standards and Guidelines for Senior Fitness, Part 2.

These Standards and Guidelines for Senior Fitness are to be used in conjunction with AFAA's *Basic Exercise Standards and Guidelines*.

A. Definitions

1. Activities of daily living—refers to activities one may perform on a regular basis, such as walking, automobile driving, traveling, housekeeping, cooking, grocery shopping, bathing, dressing, eating, and transferring.

2. Aging—refers to the regular changes that occur in mature genetically representative organisms living under representative environmental conditions as they advance in chronological age. According to Dr. Waneen Spirduso, author of *Physical Dimensions of Aging*, "aging refers to a process or group of processes occurring in living

organisms, that with the passage of time, lead to a loss of adaptability, functional impairment, and eventual death." There are different rates of aging among individuals and within the individual himself. For example, one may look old by his appearance, yet his psychological and social capacities for adaptation and change may be similar to or even more advanced than individuals half his age. In addition, a given 81-year-old man may have the ability to run longer and faster than a given 60-year-old man.

3. Gerontology—refers to the study of the normal processes of development as well as the differences found among people of all ages, their causes, and the factors that amplify or attenuate them.

B. Age Categories for the Older Adult

Middle Aged	40–64 Years of Age: the pre-retirement years
Young-Old	65–74 Years of Age: the immediate post-retirement years when there is relatively minimal functional impairment
Old Ages	75–84 Years of Age: some functional impairment but most individuals can still live somewhat independently
Old-Old	85+ Years of Age: greater functional impairment and may have institutionalized care
Oldest-Old	100+ Years of Age: greater functional impairment and may have institutionalized care

II. Benefits of Exercise for Seniors

A. Physiological Benefits of Exercise

- Increased aerobic capacity
- Decreased resting heart rate
- Decreased blood pressure
- Reduced blood serum cholesterol and triglycerides
- Increased muscle strength and endurance
- Increased muscle mass and neural response
- Improved circulation
- Reduced body fat
- Improved sleep

B. Musculoskeletal Benefits of Exercise

- Increased muscle strength and endurance
- Increased bone density
- Increased range of motion
- Increased flexibility
- Improved joint stability

- Improved balance
- Improved ease of movement

C. Psychosocial Benefits of Exercise
- Reduced tension, anxiety, and fatigue
- Enhanced feeling of well-being
- Improved self-image and self-esteem
- Opportunity for shared activity with friends
- Maintenance of independence and self-care
- Reduction of pain

III. Exercise Overview for the Healthy Sedentary Older Adult

A. Older Adult Participant Goals

1. By attending an exercise class, the older adult participant may feel a greater social and psychological accomplishment than actual physical results.

2. Older adult participants may not be as concerned with the competitive side of fitness as much as they are in the improved physical ease in accomplishing daily tasks and the heightened quality of life.

3. In the initial stages of training, exercises that are easily accomplished may be preferred to those that offer a challenge. Feelings of inadequacy are thereby avoided and the participant's confidence in his/her ability to succeed in this endeavor begins to build at the outset.

4. Older adults may prefer exercises that are repetitive over a period of time so they are able to notice improvements in coordination, balance, strength, endurance, and flexibility.

5. Not all exercises are appropriate for the older adult participant as some movements are difficult to learn or awkward to perform. Base your exercise selection on the individual's abilities in his/her exercise program.

6. Stretch more often than usual. This helps to alleviate stress and any discomfort in the surrounding joints, as well as to increase flexibility. In addition, it provides a pertinent break between more strenuous exercises.

B. Role of the Instructor

1. The fitness instructor's goals should coincide with those of the participants. The primary focus of the instructor is to improve and maintain the health of the participant in a fun and safe environment.

2. Provide class participants with education in the areas of nutrition, exercise physiology, psychology, sports medicine, and understand how each relates to the aging process. Become well-versed in common illnesses and diseases associated with aging and how they may affect exercise programming, and stay current with updates.

3. Provide, where possible, an adequate environment for the senior/older adult exerciser, including the following.
   - Easy access to the facility
   - Bright colors to enhance visual stimulation
   - Proper lighting to avoid glare
   - Proper acoustics—keeping stereo volume at an appropriate level
   - Proper heating and ventilation
   - Well-displayed large-print training charts (e.g., RPE), a large-faced clock, and other signage that may meet the needs of your participants

4. Give clear, concise instructions for each exercise. Describe the exercises generically, not specifically (e.g., "Reach toward your feet" rather than "Hold onto your feet"), to accommodate the variety of strength and flexibility levels in the class.

5. Use both verbal and nonverbal cues (hand cues) for ease of following along. Some participants may not be able to hear the verbal cue, but can see the hand cue.

6. The fitness instructor may be the one who has the greatest impact on motivating the older adult participant to long-term exercise adherence. Among other things, instructors might consider incorporating the following in their teaching experiences.
   - Maintain a professional demeanor that encompasses an unprejudiced and nonjudgmental attitude toward older adults.
   - Act as a role model for class participants.
   - Recognize individual differences in fitness and health levels.
   - Adapt exercise programs to meet individual needs.
   - Teach proper techniques, alignment, and posture.
   - Educate the participant about which exercises increase balance, strength and endurance, reduce fat, or increase flexibility. Emphasize stretching exercises for increased range of motion and flexibility; and balance, aerobic activity, muscular strength, and endurance exercises for efficiency and effectiveness in performing activities of daily living (ADLs); all of which will result in improved functional fitness and quality of life.

- Educate the participant about the positive effects exercise has on the older population, both physically and psychologically.
- Develop the physical skills of the participants.
- Be sensitive to a participant's goals as well as his/her concerns over attaining them.
- Show sincere interest in each participant and develop a rapport that leads to a relationship based on trust.
- Identify class participants who need more support or more personalized attention.
- Show sensitivity, compassion, patience, and a good sense of humor.
- Talk to a senior as an adult and not as a child.
- Return participants' praise, appreciation, and warmth.
- Design the class to include social opportunities and events.

C. Instructor Credentials

Instructors should hold the following credentials.

1. An undergraduate or graduate degree in a health- or fitness-related field (e.g., nursing, recreational therapy, physical therapy, physical education, exercise physiology)
2. Specific training in older adult fitness programming from either organizations, associations, colleges, or universities that offer such course work (e.g., California State University, Fullerton)
3. Course work in the field of gerontology
4. Certifications in CPR, AED, and advanced first-aid/emergency response

IV. Participant Screening

A. Medical Clearance

All individuals beginning an exercise program should follow the guidelines for medical clearance as stated in AFAA's *Basic Exercise Standards and Guidelines*, section V.A.5. Additionally, to avoid risk of injury to participants and litigative risk to instructors, attendance in class should be limited to those with physician approval. The primary responsibility for the individual's overall health management should lie with the physician. A close alliance between the fitness instructor and the participant's physician is strongly recommended.

B. Health Risk Appraisal

It is important to evaluate an individual's level of fitness prior to an exercise program in order to:

- determine the current level of physical fitness and overall health status;

- objectively evaluate an individual's response to exercise; and
- determine an appropriate workload when individualizing an exercise program.

C. Role of Instructor in Health Screening Process

Only qualified specialists (e.g., physicians with the assistance of exercise test technologists or clinical exercise physiologists) may assess the safety of exercise and administer an exercise stress test. Individual exercise programs may be developed by senior fitness specialists or AFAA Fitness Practitioners based on the information received from the physician and from a comprehensive health questionnaire filled out by the participant. It is again recommended that all class participant have written approval from their physician. The individual's physician who has recently completed a thorough physical and health history of a prospective participant, should be most qualified to identify an appropriate level of exercise and any limitations. The fitness instructor' major post-screening responsibility is to lead the participant's exercise program in regard to type of exercise, duration, intensity, frequency and rate of progression in a safe and effective way.

V. Special Exercise Considerations

A. Program Design

Keep in mind that the average sedentary older adult may initially have difficulty meeting the minimums of exercise frequency, intensity, and duration. The exercise training minimums should be incorporated only when the participant is physically able to accomplish them without injury, elevated heart rate, or muscle fatigue. To avoid these anxiety-producing consequences of over-exercise, a low-intensity interval training program may be considered as an option for certain individuals. This allows the instructor to alternate exercises that sustain a higher heart rate with those that do not. Balance a participant's fitness level with his/her willingness to commit time to an exercise program and always offer a range of frequency, duration, and intensity.

NOTE: The factors that need to be taken into consideration when personalizing an exercise program for individuals over 60 years of age are size, strength, flexibility, balance and coordination, orthopedic limitations, personal goals, and current health status, including the presence of risk factors. From the standpoint of compliance, the participant' time schedule and exercise preference must also be considered.

B. Joint Replacements

The instructor needs to be aware that more seniors than ever before are having hip and knee replacements. A new prosthesis allows them to participate both in routine activities of daily living and in physical exercise with minimal or no discomfort. When self-limiting pain becomes less accurate as an indicator of the extent of safe exercising, the risk of injury to the joint may increase causing loosening or dislocation of the newly implanted prosthesis. Exercise should involve only smooth, controlled movements performed cautiously and deliberately at a slow-to-moderate speed. Instructors may want to consult with a physician regarding exercises that are appropriate for knee- and hip-replacement patients.

C. Hydration

Some older adults are at greater risk of dehydration due to insufficient fluid intake and the use of diuretics for the treatment of cardiovascular disease. Caffeine and diuretics increase the body's need to urinate, and diuretics can affect the electrolyte balance within the elderly. Encourage older adult participantss to drink plenty of water before, during, and after exercise when not contraindicated.

D. Pelvic Floor Exercises

Kegel exercises work the muscles in the pelvic floor and those muscles that control urinary function. Strengthening may occur by contracting and releasing the muscles in the pelvic floor in a slow and controlled manner. These can be performed in class or at home. These exercises may help to prevent or alleviate urinary incontinence in older adults.

E. Environmental Considerations

1. Exercise programs are best facilitated in a well-ventilated area with mild temperature and relatively low humidity.
2. When exercising outdoors, the recommended temperature range is from 40°–75° F with humidity less than 60%.
3. Stay indoors on days registering high air pollution. It is preferable to exercise indoors during unhealthy air conditions.
4. Encourage participants to dress according to the weather conditions. In the cold, dress in layers to help keep moisture away from the body and cover the head to prevent heat loss. In the heat, dress in light, non-restrictive clothing that allows for proper breathing and evaporation of perspiration.

VI. Class Format, Training Principles, and Guidelines

A. Sequence

Sequence takes on greater importance with the older adult exerciser as the transition from a standing position to the floor is not always easily accomplished. It may be preferable in some cases to do the complete class in a standing or seated position to avoid the strain of lifting and lowering the body off the floor. If floor work is to be included, place it at the end of class to allow for adequate time to recover and return to a standing position.

B. Types of Movement

1. Physical activity that utilizes the large muscle groups and is rhythmic in nature (e.g., walking, dancing, cycling, swimming) is preferred for cardiorespiratory conditioning.

2. Both aerobic and anaerobic weight-bearing exercises are recommended for stimulating bone density in the senior participant. Weights are to be used only during the anaerobic/strength conditioning portion and when the participant has reached a fitness level that will enable him/her to add the extra force outside gravity alone. More information is available in Chapter 9, "Standards and Guidelines for Group Resistance Training" in this textbook.

3. Movements that work through the full range of motion and static stretching exercises that increase flexibility are beneficial for the older adult participant.

4. Physical limitations may be more prevalent in the older adult participant. Physical strength in general may be a limiting factor in and of itself. Orthopedic problems in the older adult that the fitness instructor may encounter are shoulder, hip, knee, ankle, finger, and wrist discomfort associated with arthritis. Weight-bearing activities may be alternated with non-weight-bearing activities (e.g., seated chair exercises or exercises performed in water). These methods allow avoidance of undue stress on the joints, providing support for a frail body with the added confidence necessary for the participant to successfully complete the exercise.

5. Balance is thought to be an important factor relative to the prevention of falls, which is a major concern with the elderly. Therefore, include exercises that address the multisensory systems—vision, somatosensory, and vestibular—and that focus on the four dimensions of balance (voluntary postural control, anticipatory postural control, reactive postural control, and sensory organization).

C. Speed of Movement

1. Natural changes occurring through the aging process must be taken into consideration when developing exercises for the older adult participant. Due to degeneration of joint surfaces, as well as a decrease in the amount and thickness of the synovial fluid in the joint, an increase in joint stiffness and loss of flexibility occurs with age. Muscle tissue tends to atrophy causing a decrease in size of muscle fiber and muscle strength. Reaction time tends to slows with age. Therefore, one's ability to process a given stimuli or movement pattern may decrease as will one's kinesthetic awareness and balance. With these changes occurring with age, perform all movement, including stretching, calisthenics, resistance training, and cardiorespiratory conditioning, with control and slow-to-moderate speed.

2. Speed of movement has a direct impact on the intensity of the exercise. Monitor perceived exertion to control the speed of any movement. This will directly correlate to the shape, size, fitness level, and exercise experience of the individual.

3. Allow for extra time to make the transition from the floor to a standing position or vice versa. Raising or lowering the body is accomplished best by moving slowly and carefully to avoid dizziness and injury. A chair may be utilized for support. Some older adults are not comfortable going down to the floor. Demonstrate alternative exercises that can be performed in a standing or seated position. Cue participants to use proper body mechanics when lowering themselves down to the floor.

D. Intensity and Duration

Research indicates exercise training at a low to moderate intensity (40–59% of HRR or 64–84% HR_{max}) for a longer duration (minimum of 20–30 minutes) may lower the risk of cardiovascular disease and improve the cardiorespiratory system in the mature adult. Training at more vigorous intensities (60–85% HRR and 85–94% HR_{max}) may bring optimal cardiorespiratory fitness. However, these higher intensities also increase the risk of injury to seniors. Since older adults may suffer from a wide variety of medical conditions, a more conservative approach to cardiorespiratory training should be taken. A more frequent, longer duration activity (up to 60 minutes), at a low to moderate intensity, will produce positive physiological changes within an aging body with less injury occurring. Intensities may range from 40–59% of heart rate reserve (HRR) and the duration may be limited to several 10-minute bouts. It may help lower risk of injury by gradually increasing duration versus intensity. The utmost caution should be taken during the exercise program, since exercise itself raises the systolic blood pressure during the activity. Chair aerobics has been developed as a fun and positive alternative for seniors who are unable to stand due to a degenerative disease or rehabilitation from orthopedic surgery.

E. Frequency

An exercise frequency of at least 3 days per week is recommended. Exercise frequency of more than 5 days per week and duration in excess of 60 minutes per session seem to offer the participant little additional gain in aerobic capacity, yet appears to greatly increase the incidence of orthopedic injury. However, moderate physical activity performed on most, if not all days of the week, is recommended (ACSM, 2010; USDHHS, 2008) to help maintain health. Simply staying active on a daily basis (e.g., gardening, cleaning house, shopping) helps to maintain general fitness in older adults.

Table 5.1. AFAA At-a-Glance: F.I.T.T. Summary Chart for Aging Adults

Cardiovascular Training

Health and Disease Prevention Recommendations

5–7 days per week; accumulation of 30 minutes of moderate-intensity activity

Fitness Improvement Recommendations

F: 3–5 days per week of continuous training (5 days for moderate; 3 days for vigorous; or 3–5 days of a combination of moderate to vigorous intensity)

I: Based on RPE 0–10: 5–6 for moderate; 7–8 for vigorous

T: 20–60 minutes: 30 min up to 60 min for moderate activity; 20–30 min for vigorous; or start with 10-minute bouts resulting in 2 ½ – 5 hrs/wk

T: Non-, low-, and light-impact

Strength Training

F: 2–3 days per week

I: To the point of mild fatigue typically in 10–15 reps

T: 20–45 minutes or time to complete 1–3 sets of one exercise for each major muscle group

T: Progressive static and dynamic forms of resistance training

Flexibility Training

F: Minimum of 2–3 days per week (preferably every day)

I: Edge of discomfort, holding each static stretch for 10–60 seconds

T: 10–20 minutes or time to complete 1–3 sets of one stretch for each major muscle group

T: Static and dynamic (slow movement) forms of stretching

Balance Training

F: 2–3 days per week (preferably every day)

I: To a level that challenges one's balance without continued loss of form and alignment

T: 5–10 minutes or time to complete 1–3 sets of 8–10 balance exercises

T: Static and dynamic exercises

(Adapted from ACSM & AHA, 2007, Physical Activity and Public Health in Older Adults: Recommendation from the American College of Sports Medicine and the American Heart Association; USDHHS, 2008, Physical Activity Guidelines for Americans; ACSM, 2010. *ACSM's Guidelines for Exercise Testing and Prescription*, 8th ed.)

F. Rate of Progression

- Exercise must be of sufficient duration, intensity, and frequency in order to create a training effect.
- This training effect will usually allow the individual to increase his/her workload somewhat each class.

- Each participant's exercise program needs to be evaluated and adjusted individually.
- A participant may demonstrate a slower rate of progression due to the aging process.

G. Posture and Alignment

Sedentary older adults may have alignment problems due to natural aging and osteoporosis. Therefore, older adult participants are encouraged to maintain good posture and alignment whenever possible.

H. Breathing

1. A consistent, rhythmic pattern for breathing is recommended throughout the class to avoid an increase in blood pressure. Inhale and exhale through the nose and mouth in a relaxed fashion, always exhaling on the exertion. Have seniors exhale through pursed lips to help make sure they are exhaling completely.

2. Dyspnea (shortness of breath) and hyperpnea (rapid breathing) can be associated with sedentary aging due to a decrease in elasticity of tissues and decline in function of the respiratory system. These conditions may provoke fear and anxiety, as well as emotional stress. Dyspnea and hyperpnea usually lessen or disappear over time as long as the senior participant is in good health.

3. Frequent reminders to breathe rhythmically is recommended throughout the workout (especially during static and resistant exercises).

I. Danger Signs

As part of the pre-class instruction, participants should be advised to inform the instructor of any pain or discomfort they may experience during the class. When working with senior exercisers, special attention must be paid to observing outward signs of physical distress and fatigue that could possibly lead to a more dangerous situation. (See AFAA's *Basic Exercise Standards and Guidelines*, section V.B.1.)

J. Music

Research into the effect of music on exercise performance reveals that energy expenditure generally increases while perceived exertion generally decreases when music accompanies exercise. The results may indicate that music acts as a stimulus that takes the mind away from the physical manifestations of exercise. This may have both a positive and a negative influence on the exerciser. On the positive side, music takes the participant's mind off the exercise, thereby allowing him/her to accomplish more of the workload with less awareness of discomfort or fatigue. On the negative side, the lessened awareness may cause a participant to exercise too strenuously, making him/her more prone to injury or exceeding his/her training heart rate.

For older adults, instrumental music is recommended over lyrical music, allowing participants to hear verbal cues from the instructor more easily. Music may be used for background accompaniment or for choreographed routines. When using music for choreography, make sure the tempo is appropriate for the older adult participant. When moving to each beat of the music, the following beats per minute (bpm) are recommended.

- Warm-up: 80–120 bpm (the less fit the participant, the slower the tempo)
- Cardiorespiratory conditioning: 120–149 bpm
- Major muscle strength and endurance: 118–135 bpm

Another consideration regarding music is the volume. Minimize the volume level of the music to ensure that participants are able to hear the instructor's cues. The older adult may become more sensitive to higher volume and certain pitches of sound. Those wearing hearing aids may need to adjust them according to the volume of the music.

VII. Pre-class Announcements

Follow the same pre-class announcements as for other group exercise classes. Refer to AFAA's *Basic Exercise Standards and Guidelines*, section VIII.A. Additionally, advise older adult participants to wear shoes appropriate to the activity and clothing that allows free and comfortable movement. Choice of attire should also reflect a consideration of environment, temperature, and humidity.

VIII. Warm-Up

A. Definition, Purpose, and Duration
See AFAA's *Basic Exercise Standards and Guidelines*, section VIII.B.1.

B. Methods
See AFAA's *Basic Exercise Standards and Guidelines*, section VIII.B.2.

C. Special Considerations
See AFAA's *Basic Exercise Standards and Guidelines*, section VIII.B.3.

1. Older sedentary individuals may take longer to respond to the physiological changes occurring due to exercise. Therefore, 10–15 minutes for warm-up may be more appropriate to prepare the older adult participant for the more vigorous activity to follow.

2. Incorporate psychological preparation into the warm-up by means of gradual movements and verbal motivation from the instructor.

3. Emphasize dynamic movements that utilize the large muscle groups, as well as movements that emphasize the small muscle groups found in the hands and fingers.

4. Give special attention to properly preparing the back and shoulders, hip, knee, and ankle joints for the more vigorous exercise to follow.

5. Exercises that improve body awareness, posture, and balance may be incorporated in the warm-up as well as in the cool-down. During the initial stages of exercise training, utilize support for the balancing exercises.

D. Precautions

1. Slow and controlled movements are recommended.

2. Avoid forward spinal flexion movements if known spinal osteoporosis is present.

3. Dizziness may occur if the participant closes eyes, lowers head below the heart, performs twisting motion of the neck and head, or rises off the floor too quickly.

4. Participants with prosthetics (e.g., hip or knee replacement) need to follow their doctor's exercise recommendations pertaining to joint action and range of motion.

IX. Cardiorespiratory Training

A. Definition, Purpose and Duration

See AFAA's *Basic Exercise Standards and Guidelines*, section VIII.C.1.

B. Methods

1. Low-impact aerobics (i.e., one foot remains in contact with the floor at all times), walking, stationary cycling, swimming, and a seated chair workout are the recommended methods for attaining cardiorespiratory conditioning.

2. Cardiorespiratory exercises are performed to slowly and gradually increase the intensity and range of motion of the movements in steady state then gradually decrease.

C. Special Considerations

1. Rating of Perceived Exertion (RPE)
   - Best indicator of workload tolerance during both cardiorespiratory training and recovery.

- Train at similar intensity (physiological strain), not same workload.
- Train between the "fairly light" and "somewhat hard" level or 12–14 on the Borg RPE 6–20/15-Point Scale or or 4–6 on the 10-Point Scale (refer to Table 5.1 AFAA At-a-Glance FITT Summary for Aging Adults).

2. Choreography
   - Arm and leg elevation should directly correlate with the range of motion, flexibility, and fitness level of the individual.
   - Arm and leg elevation should be varied to control heart rate and reduce the stress on the joints.
   - Combination moves requiring coordination of both arms and legs should be entered into slowly, starting with either the arms or the legs, and then adding the other.
   - Utilize only a few moves when building a combination. Keep it simple and fun.
   - Use lateral movements with caution and simplify movement patterns.
   - Repeat directions and movement patterns often.
   - Use verbal and nonverbal cues.

3. Using step exercises and equipment with older adults:
   More research is needed in the area of step training and older adults. It has been demonstrated to enhance balance, agility, and coordination in older adults. However, safety is a concern.
   - Get physician's clearance—Step choreography can be hard on hips, knees, and feet. Refer to Chapter 11, "Standards and Guidelines for Step Training," in this textbook.
   - Keep bpm low (118–120).
   - Use just the floor (no step platform) or no more than a 4-inch platform.
   - Choreography should be simple and easy to follow.
   - Provide a longer warm-up and cool-down period.

D. Precautions

1. Make sure participants know how to monitor their workloads at a comfortable pace throughout the class.
2. New exercisers often have difficulty pacing their fitness program. Be alert for signs of overexertion.
3. Monitor intensity every 4–5 minutes during the cardiorespiratory conditioning.

E. Cardiorespiratory Cool-Down (Post-Aerobic)

Recovery heart rate should return to normal levels by slowly reducing cardiorespiratory activity. Some older adults may require a longer time to allow for sufficient heart rate recovery. Time can be from 5–10 minutes. Be sure to check the recovery heart rate through perceived exertion as an indicator of whether the intensity is reduced appropriately.

X. Muscular Strength and Endurance Training

A. Definition, Purpose and Duration

See AFAA's *Basic Exercise Standards and Guidelines*, section VIII.D.1.

B. Methods

See AFAA's *Basic Exercise Standards and Guidelines*, section VIII.D.2.

C. Special Considerations

1. Strengthening of muscles of the arms, chest, shoulders, and upper back can help further prevent kyphosis and other postural deviations.

2. Weakness in the upper body is common among sedentary older adult participants (especially in women) due to lack of use and atrophy of muscles and decreased neurological response.

3. Movements should be resistive, smooth, controlled, and slow enough to allow for a complete contraction and extension.

4. Free weights may be used to bring about a more rapid muscular response. Free weights should only be introduced when the class participant is able to complete a non-weighted workout with resistance and at a variety of speeds. Utilization of free weights should begin with the lowest weight (½ to 1 lb) with additional weight being added only at such time as the senior participant is able to complete the movements and designated repetitions with ease. Maximum tension and high-resistance exercises are to be discouraged for high-risk and symptomatic individuals as well as those participants with atherosclerotic cardiovascular disease (CVD).

5. The use of elastic bands and other resistive equipment may be used for upper body conditioning when not contraindicated.

6. Stabilization exercises are recommended. If inadequate abdominal strength is present, certain torso stabilization exercises may place inappropriate stress on the spine. Properly performed stabilization exercises (e.g., abdominal hollowing, modified bridge, prone alternating leg extensions, and abdominal curls in a standing or seated position) and can be a positive compliment to traditional isotonic forms of abdominal training.

D. Precautions

1. A weighted workout is contraindicated for the individual suffering from severe arthritis. Those with mild arthritis can actually achieve improved benefit through a modest resistance training program. Work closely with the individual's physician whenever in doubt.

2. Proper breathing techniques are extremely important for older adult participants, especially those with heart disease. Holding one's breath should be avoided, as this may elicit the Valsalva maneuver.

3. Dynamic lifting and sustained isometric contractions are contraindicated for the older adult participant with hypertension due to the increase in systemic arterial blood pressure.

4. Muscular strength and endurance goals have been indicated as a more positive step toward improved quality of life for the senior participant.

Group One—Chest: Pectorals

a. Push-ups—Incorporation of push-ups should be based on the participant's strength and orthopedic limitations. Weight-supported modifications (e.g., performing push-ups against the wall from a standing position or against a chair in a seated position) may be more appropriate in the initial stages of training.

b. Cue participants to keep wrist in neutral alignment when using small poundage of weights or tubing. Many women have had reactions to latex material. Therefore, resistive equipment with handles is recommended.

c. Stabilization exercises—see AFAA's *Basic Exercise Standards and Guidelines*, section, VI.C.6.

d. Sample exercises—flys, chest press with variations and resistive tools

Group Two—Back: Trapezius/Rhomboids/Latissimus Dorsi

a. Shoulder and back precaution—in a standing position cue participants for proper alignment to maintain healthy shoulders and backs. Omit performing exercises during which the shoulder abducts and internally rotates, with the elbow higher than the shoulder (e.g., upright rows).

b. Cue participants to keep wrist in neutral alignment when using resistive tubes. Some older adults have had reactions to latex materials. Therefore, resistive tubes with handles are recommended (e.g., seated rows, pull-downs).

    c. Stabilization exercises—see AFAA's *Basic Exercise Standards and Guidelines,* section VI.C.6.

    d. Sample exercises—shrugs, overhead press, lat pull-down, horizontal seated row, upright row with variations, and use of resistive tools

Group Three—Shoulders: Deltoids/Rotator Cuff

    a. Use unilateral and bilateral variations to perform exercises for the deltoids and rotator cuff muscles.

    b. To strengthen rotator cuff, AFAA recommends external rotation with a light weight or strap. In a standing, side-lying, or seated position with the elbow remaining at the side, take the strap or a light weight through a full range of motion.

    c. Stabilization exercises—see AFAA's *Basic Exercise Standards and Guidelines,* section VI.C.6.

    d. Sample exercises—raises, overhead presses, shoulder cuff rotations with variations, and use of resistive tools

Group Four—Arms: Biceps/Triceps

    a. In a standing position, cue participants to maintain neutral pelvic alignment when performing overhead exercises and kickbacks.

    b. Perform variations of movement through a range of motion that places no stress to the shoulders.

    c. Stabilization exercises—see AFAA's *Basic Exercise Standards and Guidelines,* section VI.C.6.

    d. Sample exercises—curls, overhead exercises, and kickbacks

Group Five—Hips: Abductors/Adductors

    a. Side-lying position—abduction above 45° or shoulder height in this position may strain both the lower back.

       1) In this position, adduction exercises, which require the upper leg to cross over the working leg, may be difficult because of the range of motion and flexibility.

       2) In this position, it is recommended that the head rest on the extended arm. Supporting the upper body on elbows may cause stress to the shoulders.

    b. All-fours position—variations in this position may be difficult on a senior participant's knees or wrists.

    c. Stabilization exercises—see AFAA's *Basic Exercise Standards and Guidelines,* section, VI.C.6.

    d. Sample exercises—side-lying leg lifts, ball squeezes (supine or standing), standing hip abduction lifts

Group Six—Buttocks: Gluteus Maximus

a. Side-lying position—alternately contract and release gluteal muscles.

b. All-fours positions—variations in this position may be difficult on a senior participant's knees or wrists.

  1) With leg bent at knee, perform hip lifts, pushing one heel toward ceiling while gluteus muscles contract.

  2) To work one leg behind body at hip level, bend or curl lower leg, bringing heel toward buttocks, short level. Extend and repeat. If hip flexors are tight or participant cannot maintain torso stabilization, full extension of the hip with the leg in a long lever behind the body to hip height may be difficult. Therefore, use short-lever range of motion.

  3) Participants have the option of placing weight on elbows versus hands in the all-fours position, especially if carpel tunnel condition exists. Placing elbows on a step or chair may be more supportive than placing them on the floor to reduce stress to the lower back.

c. Standing—gluteus muscles are worked as described above by pushing heel away from body, keeping knee bent, and buttocks contracted. Squats and lunges also focus on gluteal muscles (see below).

d. Supine—alternately contract and release gluteal muscles.

e. Stabilization exercises—see AFAA's *Basic Exercise Standards and Guidelines,* section VI.C.6.

f. Sample exercises—rear leg lifts, reverse lunges, wall slides

Group Seven—Front of the Leg: Quadriceps/Hip Flexors/Tibialis Anterior

a. In a standing position, maintain neutral pelvic alignment with knees aligned over toes.

b. Lunges in a stationary position are appropriate, if executed correctly. Avoid lunges performed by walking forward alternating feet, if balance is a concern. This variation of lunge may stress knee ligaments.

c. Avoid deep-knee bends due to potential stress to knee ligaments.

d. The traditional weight lifter's squat may be too stressful due to difficulty of maintaining correct torso alignment.

e. Squats

  1) For moving squats: AFAA recommends following the same guidelines as for lunges. While moving and stationary

squats will strengthen the legs and pelvic floor muscles, many older adults may have difficulty maintaining balance without external stationary support. A ballet barre or weighted bar/stick is a good tool to help decrease balance concerns while squatting.

Movements should be slow and controlled, holding onto a stationary support structure (e.g., ballet barre throughout the squat, if needed). Use legs, buttocks, and stabilized torso as well as assistance from stationary support structure to push back to a standing position. Keep knees behind toes to prevent stress to knee ligaments.

2) For stationary squats: This is a great exercise to practice at home. It will strengthen the legs to increase the ease of functional activities throughout the day (e.g., sitting and standing). Older adults should move slowly into the squat, continuing to bend knees and hips while lowering the body no further down than the level of the hip. If it is too stressful to return with the upward phase of the squat, older adults may drop one knee to the floor into a kneeling position and use the other knee for support to push back up. Variations for the stationary squat include a wall sit/squat, leaning back onto a wall, or using a large exercise ball against a wall.

f. Lie in a supine position when performing quadriceps and hip flexor work to avoid stress to the elbows and shoulders.

g. Stabilization exercises (e.g., wall sit) may be performed, however, cue participants to breathe properly to avoid the Valsalva maneuver.

h. Sample exercises—squats, lunges, leg extensions, knee extensions, pliés with variations and tools, toe lifts, wall slides

Group Eight—Back of the Leg: Hamstrings/Gastrocnemius/ Soleus

a. Participants may want to use a ballet barre or wall for balance.

b. Stabilization exercises—see AFAA's *Basic Exercise Standards and Guidelines*, section VI.C.6.

c. Sample exercises—hamstring curls, heel raises, rear leg lifts, and reverse lunges with variations and tools

Group Nine—Front of the Torso: Rectus Abdominis/Obliques/ Transverse Abdominis

(See AFAA's *Basic Exercise Standards and Guidelines*, sections VI and VIII.D. Also, see AFAA's Standards and Guidelines for Senior Fitness, Part 2: Therapeutic Exercise Programming for the Frail, Disabled,

Nonambulatory, and/or Institutionalized Elderly, section VI.E. on "Arthritis.")

   a. Standing

     1) Due to the extreme difficulty of achieving a resistive muscle contraction while maintaining proper body alignment in the execution of abdominis/oblique work in a standing position, it is best to perform these exercises while seated or supine. The supine and seated positions also help to alleviate any stress that may be placed on the lumbar spine and the erector spinae from uncontrolled movements.

     2) When specific medical conditions do not permit an older adult to sit or lie down in a supine position, standing abdominal work may be the only alternative. Standing abdominal contractions (e.g., pelvic tilts), when performed regularly, can help to maintain or improve the abdominal muscles within a sedentary individual.

   b. Supine

     1) Support for the head should be incorporated on an individual basis. Pillows may be brought in to help minimize stress to the cervical spine for individuals who may have developed a degree of kyphosis or upper back stiffness.

     2) The use of a pelvic tilt or reverse curl for the more experienced exerciser may help alleviate any discomfort in the neck area of the senior participant.

Group Ten—Back of the Torso: Erector Spinae

   a. The ability to correct and stabilize with the abdominal muscles in order to effectively perform lower back strengthening exercises (using the erector spinae as a primary mover for spinal extension) is difficult for some older adults. However, indirect strengthening through torso stabilization exercises will increase strength, providing participants can execute the exercises correctly.

   b. Sample exercises in an all-fours position include alternate leg lifts or lifting opposite arm and leg, as long as there are no contraindications to exercising on knees and/or wrists.

   c. The prone position may be uncomfortable or cause breathing difficulties in some participants.

   d. Stabilization Exercises—see AFAA's *Basic Exercise Standards and Guidelines,* section VI.C.6.

   e. Sample exercises—modified cobra, alternate leg lifts, opposite arm/leg lifts.

XI. Flexibility Training

A. Definition, Purpose and Duration
See AFAA's *Basic Exercise Standards and Guidelines*, section VIII.E.1.

B. Methods
See AFAA's *Basic Exercise Standards and Guidelines*, section VIII.E.2.

C. Special Considerations
1. Perform static stretches with slow, controlled movements and transitions.
2. Intensity—Avoid stretching to maximum muscle length.
3. Stretching on floor allows for greatest stability and balance.
4. Observe guidelines regarding standing forward spinal flexion.

XII. Final Class Segment

A. Definition, Purpose and Duration
See AFAA's *Basic Exercise Standards and Guidelines*, section VIII.F.1.

B. Methods
See AFAA's *Basic Exercise Standards and Guidelines*, section VIII.F.2.

C. Special Considerations
1. Heart rate should have returned to a normal level. Participants should be at the lower end of the RPE scale.
2. Elevated heart rate may indicate that the participant was exercising at too high of an intensity.
3. If heart rate remains elevated for prolonged periods after cool-down, participants should consult their physician.
4. Contract the muscles in both legs. Starting with the right leg, gradually release all the tension in the toes, ankle, calf, knee, and on up the leg through the thigh to the hip. Contraction of muscles in the left leg should be maintained, thus teaching participants how to isolate specific muscles. Then reverse.
5. Deep slow breathing should accompany relaxation.
6. Vary contraction/relaxation exercises to teach awareness of tension in the major muscle groups of the upper and lower body allowing individuals to feel the difference between a relaxed or tensed muscle.
7. Verbally instruct use of imagery to aid in the relaxation process. Ask participants to imagine their bodies being supported by a cloud or all of their joints being made of Jell-O.

8. Use a soft, near monotone voice, speaking slowly and clearly when instructing relaxation. It may be useful to dim the lights. Having participants internalize pleasant thoughts and/or using soothing "mood" music, such as the sound of waves, wind, running water may help relaxation.

STANDARDS and GUIDELINES for
Senior Fitness

Part 2: Therapeutic Exercise Programming for the Frail,
Disabled, Nonambulatory and/or Institutionalized Elderly

Introduction

Standards and Guidelines for Senior Fitness, Part 2, will discuss specific exercises, concerns, and recommendations for the frail, disabled, non-ambulatory, and/or institutionalized elderly. These guidelines were written to accompany Standards and Guidelines for Senior Fitness, Part 1: Healthy Sedentary Older Adults, and to be used in conjunction with AFAA's *Basic Exercise Standards and Guidelines*. To understand this population, a brief overview has been provided on the general characteristics, the physiological, psycho-emotional, and sociological differences that set the disabled, non-ambulatory, and/or institutionalized elderly population apart from the younger, independent older adult population.

NOTE: Frailty is defined as a condition or syndrome which results from a multi-system reduction in reserve capacity to the extent that a number of physiological systems are close to, or past, the threshold of symptomatic clinical failure (Campbell & Buchner, 1997). As a consequence, the frail person is at increased risk of disability and death from minor external stresses.

General characteristics for the frail, disabled, non-ambulatory include the following.
- Circumstantial and Functional Parameters
- Census
- Application
- Typical Group Class Profile

I. General Characteristics

A. Circumstantial and Functional Parameters

These individuals attend an adult daycare facility, reside in a nursing home, other short/long-term care facility, live at home or in a private foster care setting, but are dependent on the services of relative(s) or other caregiver(s). Seventy-eight percent (78%) of persons over 85 years of age are restricted in activity due to general weakness, declining endurance, impaired balance and gait, neuromuscular complications, or recurring falls. Forty-eight percent (48%) of non-institutionalized persons 85 years of age and older require help with activities of daily life (ADL) versus 14% of persons 65–74 years of age. Functional dependency and risk of accidental injury increase with institutionalization.

B. Census

In 2004, there were nearly 4.9 million American citizens 85 years of age and older. According to the U.S. Census Bureau (2005), the population of people over 65 years of age in the U.S. was 36.3 million and is projected to increase to 86.7 million by the year 2050.

C. Application

In working with this population, the exercise professional will normally be called upon to perform in a group setting, which offers psychosocial as well as physiological benefits to the frail elderly participant. The instructor then must be adept at simultaneously managing a variety of medical and psychological disorders while prescribing and supervising exercise activities of the greatest general safety and benefit to the group. Therefore, the following program information is addressed primarily to the leader of group geriatric fitness classes. However, the principles utilized can also be applied by instructors who work one-on-one with individual clients.

D. Typical Group Class Profile

Classes include members of both sexes. Age is typically at least 75 and may exceed 100 years (certain classes may include younger members with memory deficit, disorientation, Alzheimer's disease or permanent disability resulting from accidental injury). Common medical profiles may include one or more of the following: acute hearing or speech impairment, blindness, amputation, joint replacement, crippling arthritis, obesity, underweight, sensory deprivation, extreme atrophy, advanced osteoporosis, spinal injury, insulin-dependent diabetes, Parkinson's disease, multiple sclerosis (MS), cancer, stroke, chronic obstructive pulmonary disease (COPD), cardiovascular disease (CVD), and/or mental impairment.

II. Exercise Goals For the Frail Elderly

A. Goals

- Increase aerobic power (only under the controlled conditions stated in these senior fitness guidelines)
- Increase muscular strength
- Increase muscular endurance
- Increase grip ability
- Increase flexibility
- Increase range of motion
- Prevent bone demineralization and attempt remineralization
- Decrease pressure and discomfort in abdominal region

- Improve neurological function
- Prevent falls and accidental injury
- Attempt to improve gait and balance
- Provide social contact (can be maximized through group discussion activity during rest breaks)
- Prevent or ameliorate depression, anxiety, insomnia
- Prevent or ameliorate loss of appetite

B. Additional Goals

1. Maintenance or Improvement in Activities of Daily Life—Typical activities of daily living that may be addressed: dressing, self-grooming, self-feeding, general mobility, rising from a chair or bed, and providing one's own bathroom care. Strength and stamina are also needed to engage in typical pleasurable activities, such as craftwork, pet care, gardening, picnicking, fishing, or attending other scheduled activities. Muscular declines limit functional activities of daily life more so than cardio respiratory fitness declines; training should address strength, muscular endurance, flexibility, and coordination.

2. Prevention of Disease—Typical disorders that may theoretically be prevented in part by regular exercise include: bone loss, accidental fracture, glucose intolerance, type 2 diabetes mellitus, and constipation. Regarding previously sedentary individuals in the frail elderly population, cardiorespiratory training is unlikely to prevent atherosclerotic disease; it may theoretically prevent or postpone cardiovascular events, such as thrombosis, ischemia, angina, and myocardial infarction due to positive effects on blood pressure, coagulation, and lipid levels.

3. Treatment of Disease (as Adjunct to Qualified Medical Attention)—Exercise may contribute to overall therapy in cardiovascular disease, diabetes, stroke, Parkinson's disease, osteoporosis, arthritis, chronic obstructive pulmonary disease, chronic depression or anxiety, and dementia. Exercise may improve prognosis in disease by preventing secondary complications, such as edema, pneumonia, pressure sores, contractures, and in some instances, pain.

III. Special Safety Considerations in Geriatric Exercise

A. Medical Waiver

Medical waiver is necessary for participation of the frail elderly in any form of individual or group exercise.

1. The director of nursing may opt to approve participation—for low-risk individuals based on a general activities waiver signed

by physician, in facilities offering only very low-intensity seated stretching, calisthenics, and short-distance gait training.

2. Group cardiorespiratory training—ideally, should not be attempted unless all participants have undergone pre-exercise screening, including graded exercise testing (GXT); the cardiorespiratory training program is headed by a cardiologist; appropriate monitoring equipment and specialists are readily available to measure ongoing responses during exercise; and specific written medical orders and training methods have been issued. However, ACSM does not require a physician to head a program for individuals who are even high risk (someone with a known cardiac, pulmonary or metabolic condition) on the risk stratification chart. It is only recommended that a physician approval and medically supervised test occur prior to participation in a program. Therefore, minimal requirement is for all participants to have a written physician release prior to participating in a group cardiorespiratory training program.

3. Individual cardiorespiratory training—should not be attempted unless the instructor has discussed medical history, capacity, limitations, goals and prognosis with the individual's physician and has received the physician's specific, written medical approval, including individualized exercise prescription and training methods ordered.

B. Precautions

1. Generally avoid heavy weights, isometric exercises, and progressing exercises quickly.

2. Keep movements smooth and gentle, and work at a slow-to-moderate rate of speed.

3. Do not remove physical restraints without medical approval.

4. Set wheelchair brakes so that chairs do not roll during seated exercises.

5. Take care in avoiding any bumping or jarring to affected areas: catheters, nasal prongs, tender spots or sores on problem feet or fingers, recent surgical, and injection sites.

C. Stress Signals

1. Cease exercise and have participant rest if he/she displays or complains of lightheadedness, shortness of breath, or over fatigue.

2. Cease exercise and alert medical staff at once if individual displays or complains of dizziness, severe shortness of breath, chest pain,

any sharp pain, shakiness, trembling, queasiness, nausea, throbbing head, and any unusual or suspicious symptom.

3. Constantly observe participants for any of the signs and symptoms described above. Do not simply rely on them to communicate such responses.

D. Medications

Commonly used drugs that can affect exercise tolerance include diuretics, insulin, beta blockers, antihypertensive(s), and any drugs that affect the central nervous system (CNS). Medical staff should consider these implications in approving and setting guidelines for individual training.

E. Emergencies

1. Learn and practice emergency procedures followed in facility.
2. Know location of emergency call button in (or nearest to) exercise area.
3. If a situation ever develops in which the instructor is unsure whether or not to call for immediate medical assistance, he/she should do so anyway.

See AFAA's Standards and Guidelines for Senior Fitness, Part 1: Healthy Sedentary Older Adults, section III.B. & C.

IV. Instructor Qualifications For Teaching The Frail Elderly

A. Additional Qualification Suggestions

1. Complete internship in applicable area(s), such as:
   - cardiac/stroke rehabilitation (through local hospital clinic),
   - orthopedic rehabilitation (through local hospital clinic), and/or
   - therapeutic recreation (can be studied by serving under a nursing home or adult daycare activity coordinator).
2. Attend seminars and courses on applicable topics, such as:
   - adapted sports therapy for the elderly disabled,
   - choreography and supervision of rehabilitative wheelchair dance,
   - mental fitness activities programming for the elderly disabled,
   - management and motivational techniques in geriatric exercise programming, and
   - activities management with regard to specific disease common to the frail elderly.

B. Personal Traits Needed

- Love for the frail elderly
- Unflagging patience
- Good humor
- Liveliness and warmth
- Tact
- Creativity
- The ability to encourage, motivate and reward effort

V. Teaching Aids

A. Exercise Equipment

1. Light hand weights or soup cans (from less than 1 lb to 3 ⅓ lb)
2. Scarves, kerchiefs—for limbering and ROM exercises
3. Putty, clay, rubber balls, Nerf® balls—for grip exercises
4. Thera-Band®, Thera-Plast®, surgical tubing—for muscular strengthening and endurance

B. Music

For greater flexibility and effectiveness in nursing home class management, try playing music at a low background volume solely to enhance mood and atmosphere rather than always trying to match physical movements to beat. For this purpose, music selections may include classical, gospel, big band, ragtime, show tunes, light pop, country, and boogie-woogie (music may be borrowed from local libraries).

VI. Special Physiological Considerations Regarding the Frail Elderly

A. Cardiovascular and Respiratory System Concerns

Changes within the cardiovascular and respiratory systems in the frail elderly population are likely to be more prevalent, to present more pronounced symptoms, and to appear at more advanced stages.

1. Peak stroke volume may decline—due to a reduction of heart muscle mass, reduced myocardial contractility resulting in decreased pump force, acute varicose veins and loss in general venous tone, advanced inflexibility of the aorta combined with high systemic blood pressure, and extreme skeletal muscle weakness resulting in reduced perfusion of active limbs.
2. Oxygen extraction may be impaired—due to lowered enzyme activity, critical vessel occlusions, and a declining ratio of capillary-to-muscle fiber—all of which may, in turn, adversely affect arterial-venous oxygen difference.

3. VO2max—Activities such as walking, bathing, and using a bedpan may consume 80% of VO2max in frail elderly. Climbing stairs may exceed VO2max in males and females in their 80s. Autopsies performed on 90–105-year-olds showed that 43% developed critical occlusive coronary artery disease.

4. Practical Aerobic Exercise Programming Implications
   - Conditioning can be accomplished in seated position with sustained energetic upper body movement.
   - Aerobic training is unlikely to reverse coronary heart disease (CHD) in this population, although it may provide other benefits.
   - Group cardiorespiratory training—only when participants have undergone graded exercise testing (GXT—adapted as necessary); under permanent supervision of an experienced cardiologist; with ongoing support and monitoring (blood pressure and electrocardiogram) by qualified technical personnel; and with written medical approval.
   - Individual aerobic training (e.g., assisted walking programs that meet aerobic frequency, intensity, and duration criteria —only when instructor meets personally with client's physician to discuss medical history and the physician's individualized exercise prescription, goals, and guidelines; and with written orders of a specific nature.
   - Medical staff can decrease risk of arrhythmia by diagnosing and treating typical fluid, mineral and electrolyte imbalances.
   - This population will be subject to more extreme venous pooling than other groups after strenuous exercise. In the rare instances when criteria are met so that cardiorespiratory training can be undertaken, a long and gradual cool-down is indicated to prevent syncope (temporary loss of consciousness) and orthostatic (inability to stand).
   - This population has higher drug use. Commonly used drugs that can affect exercise tolerance include diuretics, insulin, beta blockers, antihypertensive, and any drugs that affect the central nervous system (CNS). Medical staff should consider these implications in approving and setting guidelines for individual training.

B. Musculoskeletal System Concerns

Changes within musculoskeletal and body composition in the frail elderly population are likely to be more prevalent, to present more pronounced symptoms, and to appear at more advanced stages.

1. Muscular Strength and Endurance
   - In the frail elderly population, declines in lean muscle mass may affect muscular performance more dramatically. Lean mass can decline as much as 30% between 30 and 80 years of age. Strength declines appear to accelerate after 75 years of age (65% of women 75–84 years of age cannot lift 10 lb or 4.5 kg vs. 45% of women 65–74 years of age and 40% of women 55–64 years of age). Hand grip strength can be predicted to decline 21% between 30 and 80 years of age, while leg and back strength decline by 40%.
   - In very old age, there is a change in the character of satellite cells (located between sarcolemma and basal lamina of skeletal muscle fibers) and a decline in their number, which leads to a decreased, though still functioning, capacity for muscle regeneration. Therefore, although muscular injury must be avoided, muscular conditioning can safely be attempted.
   - Practical Exercise Programming Implications
     - Grip strength can be improved with squeezing activities.
     - Muscular strength and endurance gains can be successfully affected in the elderly through seated upper and lower body exercises utilizing gravity and/or low external resistance.
     - Longer training is necessary for significant improvement (in one 8-week exercise study, 40–80-year-olds all improved in muscular performance, but the gains decreased in degree with each additional decade lived).
     - Hypertrophy is not to be expected.
2. Range of Motion (ROM)
   - In the very old, ROM deficit is often secondary to injury, chronic disease and/or enforced bed rest.
   - Individuals in their 80s have been seen to increase flexibility to the same degree as individuals in their late teens with gentle stretch exercises.
   - Practical Exercise Programming Implications
     - Implement a mild, seated stretch program when not contraindicated. For example, in an 84-year-old individual with ROM of both shoulder joints limited to 20–30° in all planes, improvement occurred with gentle resistive exercises, such as: (a) placing hands behind head and rotating elbows backward, (b) moving arm within allowed ROM while holding a soup can as an added weight (approxi-

mately 10 ½ ounces), and (c) lifting a broomstick with a 1-pound weight attached.

- Implement a bed exercise program when necessary. For example, in a 74-year-old individual incapable of sitting due to hip, knee, and back contractures, successful rehabilitation occurred with cautious, conservative neck movement; rolling and reaching from side-to-side in bed; leg raises and circles; bringing knee toward chest.

3. Skeleton
   - By 80 years of age, one in three women experiences hip fractures. Exercise programming should address fall prevention through strengthening and balance exercises; gentle exercise can usually be implemented after hip surgery or replacement.
   - In addition to other well-established risks, heavy weights (or training progression that is not gradual enough) may break down bone tissue at a faster rate than that at which the tissue can recover in frail elderly persons, leading to stress fracture.
   - Simply standing has been seen to stimulate more bone remineralization than bicycle riding (because standing is weight-bearing). In group settings, non-typical members capable of standing during upper body exercises should be encouraged to do so. (When music is incorporated into classes, standing and shifting hips to the beat may also yield motivational benefits. When ambulatory Alzheimer's disease patients attend, standing may provide a positive outlet for excess, undirected energy and may be useful in the continual goal of keeping Alzheimer's disease patients satisfactorily occupied.)
   - Bone material of cervical vertebrae in frail elderly populations is subject to fracture. Contraindicated exercises include head rolls and tilting head backward—both over-compress vertebral tissue.
   - In spinal osteoporosis, back extension exercise may help to prevent vertebral fracture, whereas back flexion may be dangerous due to over-compression.
   - There are 26 bones in the human foot, many of which are tiny and delicate. In the very old, they may be extremely fragile and subject to fracture. In institutional settings many persons wear socks or slippers instead of sturdy shoes, and many facilities have tile or terazzo floors. Closely supervise seated "walking," "marching," and "running" exercise programs to ensure that participants touch down lightly.

C. Blood/Circulation Concerns

1. In malnourished individuals, due to sensory deprivation, depression or chronic disease, O_2 extraction may be paired secondary to anemia.

2. Impaired respiratory function may result in incomplete oxygenation of pulmonary capillary blood.

3. Blood flow may be redistributed, with a greater relative proportion routed to areas where O_2 extraction is limited (e.g., skin, kidneys, other viscera).

4. Practical exercise programming implications include the following.
   - Energy level will be reduced; exercise tolerance will be reduced.
   - Aerobic capacity even for low-level stretch and calisthenic activity will be reduced.
   - Frequent and regular rest intervals are indicated (and supported by population's general tendency toward dyspnea and other signs and symptoms of blood and circulation issues).

D. Metabolic and Regulatory System Concerns

1. Prevalence and incidence of incontinence increase sharply. Practical exercise programming implications: conduct classes in location with easy restroom access; assist participants to and from restroom facilities during classes if necessary; consult care plan team in order to schedule classes at times during which affected participants do not customarily have accidents.

2. Prolonged sitting increases pressure in the abdominal region which may cause discomfort. Practical exercise programming implications include exercises that cause a shift in weight and bend, stretch, and turn the trunk.

E. Neuromuscular Concerns

1. Lower extremity muscle weakness combined with neural deficit has been tentatively identified as an independent risk factor for falls. Practical exercise programming implications include exercises that engage the knee extensors (seated leg lifts, knee lifts, knee bends, leg circles; in some cases, very light resistance might be introduced).

2. Studies are being performed currently to determine whether exercise can correct balance and gait abnormalities that lead to falls. Exercise, in fact, does improve muscular strength in the lower extremities, which may reduce risk of falls. To clarify, while a young adult uses 50% of total knee extensor strength to rise from a chair,

the same activity often calls for more than 100% of an 80-year-old's strength. Training can reverse this trend but will likely do so through neurological mechanisms more so than through strictly muscular mechanisms in the aged.

VII. Psychosocial Considerations

A. Clinical Depression
Clinical depression has been reported in up to 20% of institutionalized elderly. Contributing factors may include loss of financial independence, personal property, privacy, and control over life; feelings of helplessness, loneliness, and isolation; and a tendency to withdraw.

B. Insomnia and Anxiety
Insomnia and anxiety are even more prevalent than depression among the institutionalized. Tranquilizer drugs may add to the problem by contributing to mental confusion, dependency, and drowsiness during daytime hours.

C. Practical Exercise Programming Implications
Although exercise has not been conclusively demonstrated as an effective treatment for psychosocial disorders in the oldest populations, findings regarding younger seniors can be extrapolated to support the thesis: Exercise in a group environment, when possible, is believed to be most effective by preserving social skills and by providing a sense of community and belonging.

VIII. Common Diseases or Conditions of the Frail Elderly and Their Exercise Implications

A. Multiple Sclerosis, Cerebral Palsy, Polio
1. Changing from one exercise to the next may be difficult. Allow ample transition time and plenty of time with each exercise.
2. Atrophy may be considerable and ROM reduced. Select most appropriate exercises accordingly.
3. Omit all neck exercises if individual has trouble controlling head movement (rolling motions or "floppiness" increase injury risk).

B. Stroke
1. Follow items #1–3 under section above.
2. If paralyzed on right side, use demonstration instead of verbal instructions. Keep speech patterns short, simple, and direct.
3. If paralyzed on left side, use verbal instructions instead of demonstrations. Avoid quick movements or gestures.
4. Position unimpaired side closer to action.

5. Attempt to prevent neglect of impaired side by encouraging stroke patient to use stronger limb to help impaired limb complete exercise movements.

C. Diabetes

1. If insulin shot is received before exercise, injection site area should not be worked.
2. Immediately stop exercise and summon medical assistance if speech becomes slurred, if participant appears confused or bewildered, or if he/she exhibits undue hunger or profuse perspiration.
3. Aged diabetics are subject to blindness and amputation secondary to circulatory disorder, and with strenuous exercise, are at heightened risk of metabolic and cardiovascular complications as well as soft tissue injury. Movement must be especially gentle, conservative, pleasurable, and closely supervised.

D. Arthritis

1. Encourage proper standing and seated posture.
2. Due to joint damage, do not sustain any single, fixed exercise position for long periods of time.
3. Incorporate gentle, conservative ROM exercise (may include both active and passive), but never force ROM.
4. Schedule exercise during time of day when stiffness is least pronounced.
5. Arthritis may call for an exception to the general guidelines that isometric exercise should be avoided in frail elderly population. Isotonic strengthening of muscle groups at inflamed joints can aggravate tenderness and pain. In this instance, employ slow stretching and very conservative isometric work to prevent atrophy (e.g., for a short time, gently press against a wall or down on a table to engage musculature while stabilizing and protecting affected joint). Maintain proper breathing techniques during exercise.
6. Familiarize participants with the guidelines for pain.
    *   Some aching in the muscles is to be expected and should not require altering the exercise program.
    *   Joint pain that lasts longer than 1 hour after exercise should be recognized as a reason to curtail a particular activity until pain subsides.
    *   Alternative or reduced activity, such as performing only range-of-motion exercises, is preferable to complete rest.

7. Appropriate adjustment in exercise program should be made a, dictated by the overall improvement in the participant.

8. The American Rheumatism Association established criteria fo classification of functional capacity.

Class I: Complete ability to carry on all usual duties without hand icaps.

Class II: Adequate ability for normal activities despite handicaps discomfort or limited motion at one or more joints.

Class III: Ability limited to little or none of the duties of usua occupation or to self-care.

Class IV: Incapacitated, largely or wholly. Bedridden or confinee to a wheelchair; little or no self-care.

E. Advanced Cardiovascular Disease, Chronic Obstructive Pulmonary Disease, Inoperable Tumor, Malignancy

1. Likely to become fatigued and winded quickly. Respect self-limit ing factors.

2. Encourage performance of as much medically-approved light ex ercise as individual feels capable of. Never prod into overexertion

F. Osteoporosis/Osteomalacia

1. Use extremely light resistance (or if individual is quite frail, no resistance at all).

2. Pay particular attention to employing a slow, gradual progression technique.

3. Omit all spinal flexion (neck and back). Normally, back may be extended.

G. Neurologic Disease

1. Parkinson's disease is the third leading neurologic cause of disabil ity in the aged after stroke and dementia.
   - Participants may exhibit tremor, rigidity, speech impairment autonomic disorder, unusual posture, shuffling gait, and ten dency to fall.
   - Normally may participate in general geriatric exercise program for ROM and flexibility, muscular performance, posture im provement, and coordination.
   - Schedule exercise when rigidity is least pronounced. This wil depend upon time of day medication is taken and when peak drug effects occur.

H. Cognitive/Psychological Disorder

1. Dementia may afflict up to 30% of the very old population, 85 years of age and older, as compared to only 5% of all persons over 65 years of age.

   - Individuals may exhibit disorientation as to time and place, memory loss (especially short-term), withdrawn passive behavior, aggressive disruptive behavior, inability to comprehend language and symbols (e.g., letters and numbers), and functional dependency. Alzheimer's disease may be tentatively diagnosed.

   - A general geriatric exercise program (ROM and flexibility, muscle performance, posture, coordination) may reverse the lean tissue loss classically associated with dementia which, in turn, may prevent infections, poor wound healing, immune deficiency, and increased frailty and dependence.

   - A general geriatric exercise program may reduce necessity for physical and chemical restraints.

   - A general geriatric exercise program may prevent or decrease the wandering behavior and restlessness associated with Alzheimer's disease.

   - An enclosed exercise yard may be indicated for wandering or pacing individuals.

   - Attempt to arrest chanting or repetitive behavior with diversion techniques.

   - When possible, excuse a demented participant from group class into the care of another qualified employee if he/she cannot control disruptive behavior that is likely to upset other group members.

I. Spine Injury

1. Do not stretch lower back.

2. Do not permit individual to sit in exactly the same position for more than approximately 15 minutes without a shift in weight or pressure.

3. Since there are many types of spinal column injuries, consult the participant's physician for a list of exercise do's and don'ts specific to his/her particular condition.

J. Sight and Hearing Deficit

1. In order to avoid undesirable pressure or blood flow to eyes, a person with an eye-related disorder should not nod his/her head

down low toward chest or lean so far forward that his/her head falls below chest level.

2. It may be helpful to guide the blind exerciser manually through movements until he/she recognizes verbal descriptions.

3. Seat hearing-impaired persons near group leader or stand beside them when issuing instructions. Close doors leading to kitchen work areas, residence hallways and staff break rooms to minimize peripheral noise.

K. Limb Amputation

1. Check stump occasionally to ensure against excess rubbing of skin on wheelchair or prosthesis, which could cause irritation.

2. Position unaffected side nearer action.

IX. Nutritional Considerations

In institutional settings, diet is usually supervised by a registered dietitian. However, the exercise instructor can be a more effective care team member by remembering the following.

- Water intake should be encouraged when exercising.

- Increased energy expenditure in institutionalized elderly (even with low-level seated stretch and callisthenic programs) may call for increased dietary intake since participants are inclined to have marginal nutrient reserves.

- Deficiencies in zinc, potassium, magnesium, and vitamin D are prevalent in this population and may interfere with motor performance. Qualified nutritional assessment is indicated in conjunction with any exercise program.

- Loss of appetite is a common problem among the frail elderly. Extrapolated findings obtained on younger seniors suggest exercise may be effective in stimulating appetite in the frail elderly.

Part III

Multitraining®

Standards and Guidelines for Aqua Fitness

Standards and Guidelines for Low-Impact Aerobics

Standards and Guidelines for Group Resistance Training (GRT)

Standards and Guidelines for Cardio Kickboxing

Standards and Guidelines for Step Training

Standards and Guidelines for Mat Science

STANDARDS and GUIDELINES for
Aqua Fitness

Introduction

Since land and water exercise are different, these guidelines were written to target the unique water environment and how it affects standard exercise science principles. These guidelines provide research-based information to apply to water-exercise programs for optimal training. Use these guidelines in the development of water-exercise programs, and to evaluate exercises for safety and water-specific function. These guidelines were written to accompany AFAA's *Basic Exercise Standards and Guidelines.* Together, they address basic exercise principles and how these principles may be applied best to the water environment. These guidelines were developed for the "healthy," average, asymptomatic population that is seeking improvements in cardiorespiratory endurance, muscular strength/endurance, flexibility, and body composition for general health.

I. Overview

To understand how water affects the body during exercise, it is essential for the instructor to carefully evaluate movements in the water. In order to optimize training, every movement must be designed according to the water's effect on the body. The two primary effects are (a) resistance, and (b) buoyancy.

As previously mentioned, the environment of water is different from that of land. If the instructor's task was to design an exercise program for outer space, he/she would need to examine the effect of an anti-gravity environment on the body and determine what movements create training. The same is true in designing an exercise program for water. Here, however, gravity still affects the body, and the degree varies with a number of conditions. Since the viscosity of water is greater than that of air, resistance to movement is greater in water, creating the opportunity to make an easy movement more difficult.

Instructors must also consider the complicating fact that the effects of buoyancy on the body also provide the opportunity to make some movements easier. With this in mind, poorly designed water exercises may not create an appropriate intensity that falls within the recommended guidelines for training, and fitness results may not be optimized unless the instructor truly understands water and how the body works in it.

To become a good technician and exercise designer, the instructor must examine the water environment to understand the difference in its effect when a body is submerged and when a body is moving through it. Land-based exercise science principles learned from years of research can be applied to the water environment to create a new type of training. These new aqua fitness methods require basic skills that must be learned for successful training results to occur. While the skills needed for water fitness are not as complicated, for instance, as those needed for swimming, it is difficult to achieve a training intensity without implementing them. Basic fundamental skills, when mastered, can provide the opportunity for people to take responsibility for regulating their own work intensity. This establishes the foundation for a variety of unique water movements or programs that can be included in a lifestyle fitness program.

In order to design functional training movements, keep in mind the following considerations.

- Water's properties acting on the body
- Application of standardized guidelines for land exercise supported by current research and accepted industry methods
- Exercise designs that combine the properties of water, land-exercise science, and current scientific water research to create functional "water-specific" movements that improve health and fitness levels

II. Key Terms

ACSM—the American College of Sports Medicine

Calisthenics—stationary exercises (such as standing leg lifts and push-ups) designed to build flexibility and muscular strength and endurance

Cardiorespiratory endurance—the ability of the heart, lungs, and the body to meet the demands for oxygen by the working muscles over an extended period of time

Deep water—water depth measured on a participant who is "standing" in a vertical position when the lungs are submerged (i.e., usually about armpit depth and deeper). At this depth, the feet may be touching the bottom lightly or not at all.

Flexibility—the range of motion in a joint or group of joints

Intensity progression—a method of increasing or decreasing workload by varying a component of a move to gradually change the degree or level of physical difficulty

Muscular condition—the combination of muscular strength and endurance

Muscular strength—the ability of muscle to exert force, usually measured as the maximum load that can be lifted once. Training for this component includes high loads and low repetitions.

Muscular endurance—the ability to contract repeatedly with the same force over an extended period of time, usually measured by the number of repetitions performed at a low load until muscles fatigue. Although weak muscles may not be able to sustain activities for a long period of time, greater muscular strength can support muscular endurance by helping to resist fatigue.

Properties of water—the unique characteristics of water that affect the body during water exercise, including inertia, buoyancy, resistance, and action/reaction

- **Inertia**—force must be applied to move a body from rest, stop a moving body, or change the direction of a moving body. Inertia is the resistance to change.
- **Buoyancy**—Archimedes' Principle of Buoyancy states that when a body is partially or wholly immersed in any fluid, it experiences an upward thrust equal to the weight of fluid displaced. Buoyancy encourages freedom of movement, without the fear of falling down. Participants practice large ranges of motion, and challenge both balance and recovery-to-stand skills with ease and support. Due to buoyancy, impact can be personally adjusted from about 50% of body weight at waist depth to zero in deep water.
- **Resistance**—the act of opposing a weight or force. Resistance varies with a number of conditions. Drag resistance, or form, drag relates to the surface area (shape and lever length) and smoothness of the object moving through the water. Drag force acts to oppose motion, and will increase as the size of surface area and speed of the surface increases. Surface area and speed must be considered when evaluating their effect on resistance against the body during exercise.
- **Action/reaction**—Newton's Law states that for every action there is an equal and opposite reaction
- **Shallow water**—navel-to-nipple depth, measured with the participant standing on the bottom of the pool
- **Shallow water calisthenics**—stationary movements performed in shallow water involving variations in lever (arm and leg) actions, which focus on training individual muscle groups. Movements are performed primarily "on the beat" for a specific number of repetitions.
- **Shallow water rhythmic exercises**—movements performed in shallow water in either a stationary or traveling mode. Utilizing a variety of muscle groups and cadences, they involve a number of movement sizes (large and small). Movements are paced by intensity progressions during a training time period without regard to the number of repetitions performed at a specific beat.
- **Thermal regulation**—maintenance of core body temperature by establishing a balance between metabolic heat production and heat loss
- **Water comfort**—the ability to relax and move freely through water in a vertical position without fear or panic

- **Water fitness or water exercise**—exercises performed primarily in a vertical orientation in shallow or deep water. This type of exercise program usually does not include swimming skills, which are based on efficient horizontal propulsion through the water. Instead, water exercise uses movements that amplify drag by placing the body in positions that create resistance. The goal of this water-based program is to create sufficient intensity to provide fitness training adaptations in oxygen consumption (VO_{2max}), muscular strength, endurance, flexibility, and body composition.
- **Water-specific movements**—exercises or equipment designed to amplify the properties of water by manipulating the water's effect on the body

III. Basic Principles, Definitions and Recommendations

A. Components of Physical Fitness

The four health-related components of physical fitness are addressed in water exercise programs. Targeting the training zone with specific water-exercise design is different from doing so on land. However, the goals for health are the same.

1. **Cardiorespiratory Efficiency and Endurance**

   Water exercise provides sufficient stimulus falling within the range recommended by the American College of Sports Medicine (ACSM) to elicit cardiorespiratory improvements, and may even provide higher intensities when compared to land exercise. Additionally, it was found that water adaptation and development of water-specific skills are essential before participants can optimize cardiorespiratory overload for health gains.

   Since water is resistive, it has been noted that programs using interval formats are the most effective in providing the greatest improvements while allowing participants to individualize their own intensity for comfort and safety.

2. **Muscular Strength and Endurance**

   The ACSM recommends at least two sessions of resistance training per week. The water's viscosity provides resistance with every movement, making it a resistive environment. Improvements in this area can only be measured by research studies that focus on resistance training using water as the resistance. In general, water exercise has a greater anaerobic demand (in untrained water exercise participants) and, therefore, provides muscular strength and endurance training throughout the entire session. Several studies found significant improvements in muscular strength/endurance for the upper and lower body as well as the trunk. The gains are thought to be a result of dynamic postural alignment while traveling through the water.

The most effective gains were noted during programs that allowed participants to individualize resistance by choosing their own movement speed and adding equipment as needed for overload to progress training. It's difficult to quantify the exact amount of resistance that equipment provides since the load varies with speed, surface area, and buoyancy. However, it is estimated that deep-water running in bare feet at a quick pace results in approximately 13.7 lb or 6.23 kg of resistance.

Devices, such as boots or plastic "sandals," that increase surface area are estimated to create approximately 60.7 lb or 26.6 kg of "weight." Buoyancy devices, such as foam dumbbells, are estimated to provide approximately 1 lb of "weight" for a 3-in. cube of polystyrene or 0.5 kg for an 8-cm cube. Allowing participants to select their own speed and type/size of equipment can provide an effective progression for training, similar to land weight-room work.

3. **Flexibility**
Flexibility gains for the lower back and hamstrings, during a few programs, indicate that improvements in this area are supported. However, other programs contradict these results. Further investigation of the methods used to achieve these gains needs to be conducted.

4. **Body Composition**
Water's resistance can provide an effective environment for weight management. Walking in water at the level of the xiphoid process (just below the bottom of the sternum) at 2 miles per hour requires greater energy expenditure when compared to walking at the same speed on a treadmill. Water-specific jumping jacks performed in the pool using an aquatic step elicit a higher VO_{2max} when compared to a basic step-jack move performed on land. Deep water running at 76% heart rate max compared favorably to running on land at a 9-minute mile pace, with both estimated at 11.5 kcal/minute. A 30-minute water running session could "cost" members approximately 345 kcal without the impact of land. The ACSM recommends that intensity be high enough to expend approximately 250–300 kcal per session with a 3-day/week program. Shallow water exercises performed by healthy older women (average age, 66.4 years) were found to meet the MET levels (4–5.5 METs) as recommended by the ACSM, corresponding to positive training effects for cardiorespiratory conditioning and

weight management. It was predicted that participants would
expend approximately 190 kcal per 40-minute class (working at
intensities of very light to somewhat hard). ACSM recommends
an expenditure of approximately 200 kcal per exercise session for
weight management.

Predicted Approximate Kilocalorie Expenditures for Activities	
Aquatic exercise	5.7–6.5/min
Running in chest-deep water	8–13/min
Aquatic step (plyometric-type movements using hands in the water)	6.5–13/min
Deep-water walking	8.8/min
Deep-water running	11.5–15/min

Source: YMCA Water Fitness for Health (Sanders, 2000)

B   Principles of Training

1.   Training Effect

The training effect in water is the same as that on land, taking
into consideration appropriate frequency, intensity, and duration.
Training should be consistent, progressive, and specific. A training
effect will occur if the exercise is sufficient in all of the following
areas.

- Frequency (number of exercise days per week)
- Intensity (degree of physical stress)
- Duration (length of time)

Due to buoyancy, impact in water is decreased. Participants can
regulate their intensity by simply slowing down while continuing
the work. This creates active rest phases as needed "on demand."
This instant regulation of intensity may allow a participant to
extend the period of time spent exercising in water when compared
to a program performed on land using constant forces of gravity.
Less impact may also make it possible to exercise more frequently
without increasing the risk for overuse injury. By developing rest/
work skills, some people may increase their total exercise time,
thereby contributing to a higher level of activity and greater calorie
expenditure during the week, month, and year.

2.   Overload Principle

The exercise principle of "overload" applies in the same way in
water as on land. How this principle is applied will be addressed in
section IV.F. of these aqua fitness guidelines.

3. **Specificity of Training**

   The basic guidelines for targeting flexibility and cardiorespiratory and muscular endurance are the same in the water as they are on land. However, in water the properties of buoyancy and resistance are used to create progressions that specifically target each objective. Buoyancy supports the body through ranges of motion that can improve flexibility and helps decrease impact, allowing the large muscles of the lower body to work vigorously for both cardio and muscular training. Accommodating resistance (i.e., the harder one presses, the harder water presses back) provides challenges for muscular and cardio overload. Specific guidelines are provided in section IV of these aqua fitness guidelines.

4. **Mode of Exercise**

   Mode of exercise in these guidelines refers only to water-based programs. These programs may be formatted in a number of ways to target types of training, such as cardiorespiratory endurance or muscular strength/endurance. Various types of exercise workouts may include intervals, continuous muscular endurance work using a high number of repetitions, or flexibility work that targets stretching.

C. Improving and Teaching Fitness

1. **Improving Fitness**

   On land, the recommended frequency for improving fitness is four to five aerobic workouts per week. It is further advised that beginning exercisers start their program with three exercise sessions per week until they are accustomed to the program.

   Due to buoyancy, it is simple to regulate the intensity of the workout in water by reducing the movement speed, making the movement smaller, or allowing buoyancy to support the body for a rest. These variations can sometimes be made while still continuing the movements with the class. Compared to movements on land, most movements in water are performed with less impact to the joints and skeletal system, and the cooler water environment may reduce fatigue created by overheating.

   Beginning exercisers may adjust comfortably to their water-exercise program by applying skills to regulate intensity. Thus, they may be able to increase their frequency and duration of exercise more quickly than with land exercise.

2. **Maintaining Fitness**

   See AFAA's *Basic Exercise Standards and Guidelines*, section IV.

Maintaining fitness is accomplished by participating in a minimum of three workouts evenly spaced throughout the week. Detraining occurs within 2 ½ weeks or less following cessation of exercise depending on the fitness level at the time of exercise cessation.

3. **Overtraining**

See AFAA's *Basic Exercise Standards and Guidelines*, section V.B.4. The body needs time to rest, recover, and rebuild from the stress of vigorous exercise. Instructors and participants should be aware of the symptoms of overtraining that apply to both land and water exercise. Additionally, water exercisers need to monitor their skin and add extra lotion or Vaseline while the skin is still wet (e.g., after a shower) to keep it healthy, if necessary. Shoes are recommended for shallow-water workouts.

4. **Teaching Fitness**

The same guidelines for land instructors apply to water instructors. Water instructors may do all or most of their teaching from the pool deck and are working with gravity. It is important to note that deck instructors always wear shoes, work safely using low-impact moves, and take special care to prevent dehydration by drinking water and cooling off occasionally with a dip in the pool. High air temperatures and humidity make deck teaching difficult. When microphones aren't used, voice overuse is a common problem in a hot, humid, noisy environment.

As an instructor, be aware of the symptoms of overtraining as outlined for land exercise (see AFAA's *Basic Exercise Standards and Guidelines*, section V.B.). Individual differences in the number of classes per week an instructor can teach without risk of overtraining depends on the following variables:

- level of fitness;
- amount of time spent on the deck, as well as intensity and level of demonstration;
- amount of time spent and level of intensity demonstrating in the water;
- support equipment available (e.g., a microphone);
- pool environment, air temperature, humidity, and exposure to the sun;
- pool water condition and its effect on the skin; and
- other fitness activities outside of class.

Due to the variations in teaching methods, it is difficult to provide set guidelines. The greatest stress on group instructors during water exercise is to the voice, since pool acoustics tend to be poor, noise levels high, and microphones not as readily available (compared to land). The degree of voice use as well as the instructor's response to other variables should be used as a gauge to set the number of classes taught.

Twelve classes per week should be the maximum for the experienced instructor. Check for potential voice overuse and fatigue in setting own guidelines.

D. Teaching Methods

To maximize teaching effectiveness while minimizing personal risk, a variety of teaching methods can be used in water exercise. The following section examines the pros and cons of some teaching methods for water fitness classes. Instructors must choose a technique that is effective, safe, and best meets the objectives for the class.

1. **Method 1: Teaching From the Deck**

   Pros: It's easy to see participants and provide feedback. Participants can see moves easily. It provides quick visual cues with less instructor voice stress. The instructor can observe participants and pace the workout according to their fitness level. New participants tend to learn the skills more quickly with visual and verbal teaching.

   Cons: It's difficult to mimic water moves on land safely and effectively. High air temperature and slippery surfaces can be dangerous.

   Tips: • Demo moves at "water speed."
   • Always wear shoes with traction and impact protection.
   • Adhere to land-training guidelines for safety.
   • Keep all movement low impact.
   • Coach, lead, and cue, but don't do!
   • Check participants' neck alignment; work away from the pool edge if the necks of those in the front line are hyperextended.
   • Work on training mats, if available, to reduce impact.
   • Use an aid, such as a chair or stool, for mimicking suspended moves.
   • Wear clothing that is professional and comfortable. Clothing should provide protection outdoors and allow heat to escape indoors.
   • Don't yell! Use a microphone if possible.
   • Demonstrate a move. Then use visual cueing to have participants "continue the movement" while coaching them along without actually performing the

move. Provide feedback, motivation, and visual cues to change the move during the progression.

- Occasionally cue close to the water's surface to allow participants to maintain proper neck and head alignment. If participants have to keep their eyes glued on a deck instructor, their necks may stay hyperextended throughout the workout. When they learn the intensity progression, they can be encouraged to look at each other while keeping their neck in neutral alignment.

2. **Method 2: In-Water Teaching**

Another method participants may enjoy is teaching from the water. Remember, participants can't see the instructor's submerged body, so use exercise descriptions delivered verbally to participants along with visual cues for support. Participants must master the moves before the instructor can teach effectively from the water.

Pros: The instructor shares the workout environment with the participant. Hands-on teaching can assist participants with learning to trust buoyancy and provide one-on-one corrective feedback for skills improvement. It's a safer, more fun environment for the instructor. It may be motivating for the participant to exercise with the instructor.

Cons: It's difficult for the instructor and participants to see the lower body. Verbal teaching becomes more important, and it may be difficult for participants to hear and quickly understand the exercise descriptions. New participants may have a difficult time keeping up with "seasoned" participants who understand the skills.

Tips:
- Wear shoes that provide good in-water traction.
- Keep verbal cues concise and audible.
- Perform visual cueing signals high enough above the water for everyone to see, and be sure participants understand what the cues mean.
- Wear colored tights so you can be clearly seen by all participants, and move through the class providing feedback.
- Ask participants, "Where do you feel the work?" to check for proper exercise execution (since it's hard for the instructor to see participants now, too).
- Tell participants where they should feel the work.

- As participants become more skilled, this method becomes more effective and will probably be more fun for the instructor. By mirroring participants, the instructor will feel their intensity level, share their workout experience, and give them support by "matching their moves." Say to the class, for example, "I'm with Molly now." Everyone has permission to work at his/her own pace.

3. **Method 3: Combination Method**

Many instructors combine in-water teaching with on-the-deck demonstrations. It is a good balance for instructor comfort, safety, and fun. But transferring from the deck is difficult. Measure the pros and cons for each of the methods previously discussed and dovetail the best from each technique. The more skills an instructor's participants understand, the more flexibility he/she will have to be in the water with them.

Tips:
- Wear shoes that provide impact protection and have good traction when wet.
- Be sure to use safe entrances and exits during transitions.
- If the instructor's back is turned away from participants, be sure the lifeguard is alert.
- Deck-teach advanced or new skills.
- Before beginning a transition, cue participants to "continue the move" so they don't stop working.
- Allow time to adjust to gravity before beginning deck demonstrations.
- Allow time to adjust to buoyancy when re-entering the pool.
- Plan in advance the deck moves to demonstrate, but be flexible enough to ask participants during class, "Do you understand the move?"
- If there are new participants, deck-demo more than water-teach until they master the basic skills and understand the cues.
- Ask participants if they understand the movement during in-water instruction.
- Wear clothing that provides comfort when wet outside of the water and presents a professional appearance without a lot of readjustment during transitions.

E. Additional Idea: Pre-Class Skills/Class Demonstrations

This technique is recommended for teaching new participants the basic skills they'll need to master for effective water exercise. With participants on the pool deck and the instructor in the pool, the instructor can demonstrate and explain the skills. Participants get a deck view of the actual skill performed in water and will be better prepared to perform the skill when cued. Allow participants to ask questions.

Motivation: Motivation and proper skills performance in water are critical to achieving intensity levels sufficient to elicit training adaptations. Unlike on land, a person who simply mimics movements in water without applying force may be working at a lower intensity than required. On land, when participants lift their knees up, they all lift against a given load provided by gravity. In water, the force with which a person lifts his/her knee will determine the load provided by resistance and the amount of buoyancy assisting the leg upward. On land, the leg drops back to the floor effortlessly, but in water, depending on the buoyancy of the leg, the person pushes the leg back into position. That force in water needs to be personally initiated to avoid cheating.

Wide variations in VO_2 (oxygen consumption) responses were demonstrated in two studies speculating that the results were due to higher motivation, enthusiasm, and higher skill level of some of the subjects. The results imply that teaching and motivation techniques used by the instructor may affect training results.

Conclusion: An instructor should choose a safe teaching style that works for him/her and for the group. Education and skill development will empower participants with information so that they can take charge of their own workouts and the instructor can enjoy being their coach.

F. Muscle Balancing

See AFAA's *Basic Exercise Standards and Guidelines*, section VIII.D.3.

1. Principles for Muscular Balance (Land vs. Water)

The same principles for muscular balance that apply on land also apply to training in water. In water, the resistance is multidimensional, providing the opportunity for both the upper and lower body to work in many planes. The arms and legs each have different buoyancy based on body composition and lever length, and this must be considered during muscle conditioning exercises. If the arm is "positively buoyant" or "floats," buoyancy will assist movement upward and provide some resistance to movements downward. For example, during elbow flexion/extension, commonly called a biceps curl exercise, the type of work changes in water and with the equipment used. What follows is a closer look at a standing biceps curl utilizing an iron dumbbell on land and a buoyant (e.g., foam) dumbbell in water, as well as using a webbed glove in water.

When the move is performed on land while holding an iron dumbbell, the following muscular responses occur.

Biceps: Concentric contraction during elbow flexion
Eccentric contraction during elbow extension

The same movement performed in water holding a foam dumbbell produces the following response.

Triceps: Eccentric contraction during elbow flexion while resisting buoyancy
Concentric contraction during elbow extension

The same movement targets a completely different muscle group in water. If, instead of a foam dumbbell, webbed gloves are worn in the water during the same move, the work changes again.

Biceps: Concentric contraction during elbow flexion
Triceps: Concentric contraction during elbow extension

Instructors must analyze the water's effect on movements to determine what muscle group is being used and how. Intensity for water movements relate to resisting against buoyancy (with foam dumbbells) or applying a combination of surface area and speed (with webbed gloves) to the movement for overload. To achieve maximal speed during the full range of motion, the curl movement should begin at the surface of the water for maximum range of motion for developing speed (by applying more force) in order to maximize intensity. On land, when a weight is picked up, weight is added immediately. In water, overload must be created through range of motion, speed and surface area, or buoyancy.

2. **Muscle Balancing and Posture**

The training adaptations for water exercise are the same as they are for land. In addition, water provides liquid resistance for "on-demand" work in most planes of movement (i.e., the resistance of movement performed at an average speed in water is estimated to be approximately 12–15 times that of air-based exercise, given that water is 800 times more dense than air). The water is also constantly pushing and pulling on the body, and participants must be coached to correct trunk alignment for balance. In order to maintain a stabilized torso, achieve a balanced posture, and avoid the risk of low-back pain, muscles must be balanced in both strength and flexibility. In water, some of the applications are as follows.

- Trunk strengthening for the abdominals and erector spinae can be accomplished by performing vertical "abdominal compressions" or stabilization against the resistance of water moving against the body.

Application: During water work, balance is accomplished by contracting abdominals and erector spinae to counteract the forces of moving water against the body. This continuous work in many planes has been shown to produce significant gains in abdominal muscular endurance. Cue participants to tuck the hips under slightly to protect the back during travel backward against resistance, and hold abdominals tight during travel forward to resist against the force pushing the hips backward. These muscular contractions will train the abdominals using constant vertical compression work instead of the usual land "crunches." Instructors must cue to constantly remind participants to maintain correct posture so they don't relax and allow water to float the hips into hyperextension. Both the abdominals and erector spinae are conditioned during travel moves, providing muscle balance.

- Back and hamstring flexibility in water can be improved by "yielding" to buoyancy. That is, trusting it to support larger movements (without fear of falling down) than possible to perform on land.

- The iliopsoas can be lengthened and released during water exercise by working leg movements to the back of the body. It is easier to maintain balance during these exercises when in the water. Specific stretches can also address this area.

- Proper body alignment will contribute to more effective exercise performance while enhancing abdominal/erector spinae muscular conditioning.

- Although maintaining muscle balance is key in every workout, the recommendations for functional fitness are shown below

Strengthen:	Stretch:
Shins	Calves
Hamstrings	Quadriceps
Abdominals	Chest (Pectorals)
Low Back (Erector Spinae)	Hamstrings
Rhomboids and Trapezius	Neck
Triceps	Deltoids
Inner Thigh Adductors	Iliopsoas
Latissimus Dorsi	

- Balance and posture in water MUST be constantly cued because water acts against the body differently with each exercise.

- To maintain vertical alignment, muscle isolation occurs during stabilization against the forces surrounding the body.
- Hyperextension of the knee may occur when the knee and hip are extended during a pull-down move from the surface to the pool bottom. Slightly flex the knee to avoid the effect of water's resistance upward against a locked knee.
- Arching the back in water may occur when the hips are allowed to float backward, especially when traveling forward. If the participant has a high amount of body fat on the hips, this may be a natural tendency. Cue participants to maintain neutral alignment. See AFAA's *Basic Exercise Standards and Guidelines*, section VI.C.
- Both the back and abdominals are important for effective posture. Resistance training for these areas, by moving the arms and trunk through the water, has been shown to be effective. Be sure to use water-specific movements that maximize the water and movement for optimal and purposeful training.
- In order to achieve muscle and joint balance, movements must be worked around the body and joints. Due to the high resistance of water, it is advisable to alternate joint use during sequential muscle overload training. For example, if the biceps muscle has been worked, load resistance on the elbow joint next by working the opposing triceps muscle. Or, choose a group like the pectorals that requires primary work by the shoulder joint. Sequence muscle balance with regard to joint use and alternate to allow some rest. Remember, however, to work all the muscle group pairs.

G. Body Alignment

See AFAA's *Basic Exercise Standards and Guidelines*, section VI.C.

The same principles for body alignment on land also apply in water. However, since water buoys the body upward, allowing larger movements, alignment is more dynamic. Keep these tips in mind for water body alignment and balance.

1. Work the arms and legs in opposition. As the legs are kicking backward, push hands through the water forward to balance the lever.
2. Always use hands to create a "stable base of support." Due to action/reaction, pushing downward through the water results in the body being assisted upward. By using hands on the surface of the water, pressing downward and "sculling" (a figure 8 movement like smoothing sand), the upper body is supported so the body's base now includes at least one foot and two hands in shallow water.

In deep water or "suspended" in shallow water, the hands can provide enough support to maintain vertical position with the head above the surface.

3. Tuck the navel in and pull it up to cue contraction of the abdominals during all movements.

4. During backward rocking motions, place the hands behind the back for balance and control, and keep one leg forward to control the work of the erector spinae and assist with recovery forward. During rocking moves, limit backward motion to a comfortable range as defined by each participant.

H. Speed, Isolation, and Resistance

The following section addresses water workouts and the elements that affect resistance levels and intensity progression. These components include (a) water depth, (b) water temperature, (c) speed, (d) surface area, (e) time, (f) travel, and (g) buoyancy.

1. **Resistance**
    *   Water Depth
        The depth you choose will depend on your facility, the objective of the workout, availability of equipment, and the skill level of your participants and their body composition. Participants can work in three depths of water: (a) shallow (navel-to-nipple), (b) transitional (nipple to top of the shoulder), and (c) deep (any depth in which the feet cannot touch bottom). In chest-deep water, participants have a difficult time overcoming the surrounding water currents, resulting in slower speeds and lower heart rates when compared to shallower water (navel to nipple depth). There is evidence suggesting that participants must be able to control their movements during shallow-water exercise without buoyancy negating their efforts to develop speed. Navel to nipple-deep is recommended for most people. If participants are too deep, the work will seem easy. If a person is too shallow, the impact is increased. Finding an individual depth-to-balance gravity and buoyancy allows participants to use appropriate speed to control intensity through water. Deep water exercises are designed differently from shallow water exercises, and control over buoyancy depends on the type and application of buoyancy gear.
    *   Water Temperature
        The temperature of the water will dictate exercise design. There is a neutral temperature at which metabolic heat generated by exercise can be transferred to water without creating an energy

cost due to shivering. Maintenance of this thermal balance is important for maximizing optimal training. Exercising with a cool core body temperature can decrease oxygen transport and affect muscular coordination, cardiovascular adjustments, blood flow, intensity, and exercise performance. In shallow water, the temperature at which heat loss equals heat production for vigorous vertical exercise would be about 29° C (84° F). To maintain comfort and optimize conditioning, participants should be encouraged to keep moving continuously and wear extra clothing. It is recommended that facilities maintain a water temperature of around 28–29° C (82–84° F).

- Speed

  Due to viscosity, water provides accommodating resistance to work. By increasing the speed of movements through the water, drag and the muscular force will increase. Unlike on land, the participant also has the force of water acting against the body as well as the force necessary to move the body through the "liquid weight" of water. For example, when walking and jogging in waist-deep water, approximately ½ to ⅓ the speed of land walking/jogging is needed to equal the same level of energy expenditure. This is due to the muscular force required to move through water. Instructors used to teaching at land speed must slow down to accommodate the water.

- Speed and Surface Area

  Speed cannot be considered without regard to the surface area moving through the water. Work intensities in water are affected proportionately by the surface area moving and the speed of that action determined by the level of muscular strength. Surface area equipment provides resistance in all directions through the water, and along with speed, can dramatically affect overload (e.g., webbed gloves, fins, non-buoyant dumbbells, parachutes).

- Time

  Biomechanical analysis of movements videotaped under water indicates that it takes about four repetitions of a single movement to achieve balance and coordination and maximize range of motion. It is recommended that a single move be manipulated through a series of variations that will progressively affect intensity by incorporating the properties of water.

- Travel

  Travel in water creates frontal resistance and form drag, and creates greater resistance to movement, thereby increasing the intensity of work. A number of studies indicate that oxygen consumption is highest in water when subjects travel through it.

- Buoyancy

    If buoyancy is added for intensity variations, the instructor must examine the direction of resistance against buoyancy (assisting movements upward), the length of the lever (arm or legs), and speed of movement. Buoyancy equipment (e.g. buoyancy dumbbells, belts, noodles) may also change the shape of the limb or body moving through water, creating some form drag, which may increase resistance. However, if speed is slow, this effect may be minimal. Each exercise must be evaluated for the effect of buoyancy on the body and its effect on intensity. Be sure the water depth provides the opportunity for full range of motion below the surface.

2. **Intensity**

    The intensity progression provides the application of the proper ties for regulating resistance levels. In water, intensity is regulated by manipulating resistance and buoyancy to create work and rest. In order to regulate resistance on the body, the following intensity progression applies the principles of speed, surface area, and travel.

    The Resistance Intensity Progression

To Increase Intensity	To Decrease Intensity
Increase speed	Stop traveling
Increase surface	Slow down
(enlarge the move, increase	Decrease surface
range of motion)	(make move smaller,
Increase the speed more	decrease range of motion)
Travel the move	Slow down more
Increase speed of travel	

I.   Full Range of Motion

The land principles also apply to water during muscular endurance strength work. However, since range of motion is used to manipulate overall intensity, it may be necessary to decrease the range of some moves during cardiorespiratory conditioning to stay within a target range and be able to continue the work. Research has shown that there may be a relationship between a minimum level of muscular endurance and the ability to achieve cardiorespiratory improvements. Due to the high viscosity of water, participants may need to target muscular endurance in order to maintain appropriate intensity for a long enough duration to achieve cardiorespiratory gains. People who are highly conditioned in cardiorespiratory fitness may need to develop greater muscular endurance to overload in water for additional aerobic conditioning.

J. Functional Training

A new area of study investigates how and if water training results in better functional performance on the land both for athletes and older adults or people with chronic conditions. The research indicates that there is a positive relationship between pool training and land performance. Several studies found that runners who trained in the deep water maintained or improved their running performance on land.

In clinical studies, athletes who participated in water rehabilitation and post-rehabilitation had better scores on postural sway and fewer episodes of re-injury. In water, strengthening begins sooner, impact is adjusted and progressive, and athletes returned to competition sooner.

In older adults, water exercise participation showed significant functional improvements in flexibility, agility, muscular strength/endurance, and cardiorespiratory endurance, along with psychological well-being.

For participants with rheumatic diseases, training in water resulted in significant gains in active joint motion, reduced pain, and improvements in daily activities of living.

For individuals with other chronic conditions, such as arthritis and low-back pain, aquatic exercise programs in warm water increased balance with reduced postural sway in women, and demonstrated less back pain and improved quality of life.

IV. Class Design and Format

A. Sequence

This is a guideline for class design and format that is physiologically sound and effective, and can be adapted to fit most club policies or personal preference. The following is a recommended sequence for a class lasting approximately 1 hour.

B. Shallow Water

1. Pre-class Instruction and Equipment Orientation
2. Warm-up (3–5 min)
    Purpose—to provide a balanced combination of rhythmic limbering exercises, active stretching, and water-adjustment skills, including sculling and recovery to a stand. Easy, continuous movements should be vigorous enough to produce heat for warmth and thermal regulation. Pace the warm-up according to the pool temperature. Instructors should check proper water depth and direct rehearsal of some balanced basic moves that will be used during the workout.

3. Cardio Warm-up (2–3 min)

Purpose—to practice traveling moves using proper body align
ment and adjustment at a lower intensity, practice sculling to assi
propulsion, and continue to increase core body temperature an
slightly raise heart rate.

4. Conditioning Phase (20–40 min)

Purpose—to target training to meet fitness goals. It is importar
to remember to keep the body moving and warm for optim
training. Workouts can be targeted for cardiorespiratory endur
ance, muscular strength/endurance, or a combination of both.

C. Cardiorespiratory Training

1. Duration: Perform continuous movements for a 5–8-minute ca
diorespiratory set. Link sets to comply with ACSM guideline
Intervals of "go hard/go easy" segments allow participants to wor
and rest to prevent fatigue. Intervals can be timed or based o
participants' RPE (rating of perceived exertion). Suggested inter
vals may include 45 seconds work/15 seconds rest, or 30 secono
work/30 seconds rest.

2. Intensity: Maintain an intensity level that allows continuous exer
cise performance, coordinating both arm and leg work for aero
bic conditioning according to the ACSM guidelines. Focus on th
lower-body work for cardiorespiratory fitness. Before becomin
breathless, lower the intensity by manipulating moves in the in
tensity progression. Change to a new move before the workin
muscles fatigue.

3. Active Rest: Continue the movement at the lower end of the pro
gression or perform a resting jog/scull.

4. Monitor Intensity: Use the talk test, or a combination of the tal
test and heart rate, or talk test and perceived exertion.

D. Muscle Conditioning

1. Primary Groups: Perform 8–25 repetitions, or until targeted mus
cles begin to fatigue.

2. Active Rest: Easy jog and scull (15–30 seconds); repeat the se
quence (1–5 sets).

3. Intensity: Work at the highest personal level in the intensity pro
gression at "moderate" to "somewhat hard." Actively rest and re
peat the sequence as needed.

4. Monitor Intensity: Perceived exertion for muscular fatigue.

5. Assisting Muscle Groups: Enhance overload by providing spee
and help to keep the body warm.

6. Alternate joints being "loaded" to reduce stress. If the biceps are targeted (loading the elbow joint), the next upper-body exercise should target a group such as the pectorals, which loads the shoulder joint.

E. The Intensity Progressions

1. Upper-body Applications

   Use webbed gloves or hands for support (slice and web softly for balance only). Aerobic conditioning depends on the lower body creating the work. When the arms are added, heart rate may elevate artificially.

2. Lower-body Applications

   Perform a sequence of moves using the intensity progression. To maintain intensity, vary movements before muscles become fatigued, but allow enough time for participants to balance and develop a movement so water can act against the body to create training.

F. Equipment Application for Overload in the Progression

Various equipment designed for water exercise can further amplify the effect of water's resistance on the body. Basically, equipment falls into one of the following categories:

- buoyancy enhancement;
- surface area enhancement; or
- a combination of buoyancy and surface area adjustment.

Instructors must evaluate the purpose for each piece, design movements based on the properties of water and principles of exercise science, and evaluate each for function and safety before adding it to the program. Each piece of equipment will have its own program or movement types. Some common equipment for "overload" includes:

- buoyancy (e.g., foam dumbbells, belts, tubes);
- surface area (e.g., webbed gloves, fins); and
- combination (e.g., "sloggers," or giant sandals, foam cuffs worn on the ankles).

The aquatic step used during shallow water workouts affects intensity by allowing participants to increase range of motion and speed. In addition to providing a small shallow water area that allows participants to add more gravity to the work on the step, the aquatic step also provides the safe cushion of the deeper water for recovery off the step.

G. Cool-Down: (2–3 min)

Purpose: To promote gradual reduction in cardiorespiratory function while maintaining body warmth with light, easy, buoyant movements.

H. Active Stretching and Warm-Down: (3–6 min)

Purpose: To increase range of motion, relax, and exit the pool feeling warm. Stretching may be performed here if the water temperature allows no significant body cooling. By sculling with the upper body during lower-body work and jogging during upper-body work, body warmth can be maintained. The warm-down provides easy, light buoyant movements that allow the body to warm back up so participants leave the pool without feeling chilled.

I. Deep Water

1. Equipment orientation and safety skills check
   Purpose—To check deep-water comfort and safety skills, and teach equipment application. Participants should be comfortable in deep water, be able to perform recovery to a vertical position, and be able to tread water or "swim" their way to the side of the pool before being allowed to go into the deep end, even with equipment on.

2. Warm-up (3–5 min)
   Purpose—To learn adjustment and balance with equipment, to learn buoyancy, and to adjust to water temperature.

3. Stabilization and sculling (3–5 min)
   Purpose—To practice trunk alignment in various body positions and assist balance using sculling skills.

4. Cardiorespiratory Warm-up (2–3 min)
   Purpose—For participants to practice body alignment and locomotion methods during travel moves.

5. Endurance Conditioning (20–40 min)
   Purpose—To target training for specific fitness goals.

6. Active Stretch and Warm-down (3–8 min)
   Purpose—Same as shallow water (see section IV.B. in these aqua fitness guidelines).

7. Transition to shallow water (if possible) and perform easy, shallow-water moves without buoyancy or resistance equipment (2–3 min).
   Purpose—To prepare participants for gravity and decrease intensity further.

V. Class Level

As previously mentioned, each participant will respond differently to water based on body composition, body fat deposition, skills, and fitness level.

Therefore, coach to allow participants to work at their own pace by teaching them the intensity progression and encouraging them to adjust the components to match their own body composition, skills, and fitness level. Since intensity is regulated in water by using speed, encouraging participants to work on the beat of either the music or the instructor's counting is not advised. Individualize the workouts by teaching skills and giving feedback for motivation and improvement without driving the pace. Music can be used to provide an atmosphere of fun and encouragement, but must not dictate movement speed.

VI. Instructional Methods, Concerns, and Responsibilities

See AFAA's *Basic Exercise Standards and Guidelines*, section V.B.

A. Monitoring Purpose
1. Maximizing exercise effectiveness
2. Injury prevention
   The same guidelines listed for land apply in water, with the following additions.
   - Panic—wide eyes, stiffness, obvious fear of water
   - Body core cooling—shivering, blue lips, pinched face, and hands folded over the chest to stay warm

B. Cueing
All of the same principles for land apply to the water with some additional considerations. Water instructors leading from the deck must not try to participate in the exercises. It is impossible to perform a water workout perfectly on the deck, and the instructor should focus on teaching participants instead of personally working out.

Allow time for the participants to practice or "mark" the move. Then, coach them through the intensity progression and watch carefully to provide corrective feedback. To protect the voice, instructors should use a microphone or hand signals.

VII. Legal Responsibilities

See AFAA's *Basic Exercise Standards and Guidelines*, section V.A.

Legal responsibilities are the same as those for land with the following amendments.
- Aqua fitness instructors should complete training that tests both theoretical knowledge and performance skills for the application of land-based exercise methods to the water environment, combining the sciences of exercise and water.
- Aqua fitness instructors should have a basic knowledge of emergency water-safety skills and be able to assist with the response in the event of a water emergency.

- The recommends having a lifeguard on duty during any activity in the pool area. If this is not possible, the aqua fitness instructor must hold a current certification in lifeguard training and CPR/AED, and have an emergency action plan developed for each facility.
- The facility must provide basic safety equipment along with a safe environment, including balanced water chemicals, clear water, a clean facility, and appropriate water temperature.

VIII. Pre-Class Procedures

See AFAA's *Basic Exercise Standards and Guidelines*, sections V. and VIII.A

A. Medical and Health Considerations

All the land-based items apply with the following additions. Individuals should not be encouraged to participate in water exercise if they have diminished respiratory functions or capacity, suffer from bladder or vaginal infections, or have been diagnosed with severe hypotension. Additionally, individuals who suffer from known allergies, who have an infectious disease, or who have post-surgery open wounds (including a recent episiotomy) should be discouraged from participating in water exercise. Check with the local health department for additional medical restrictions.

Finally, a person who is afraid of water will not relax enough to enjoy and benefit from a water-exercise program. Panic is a leading cause of drowning, and it can occur even in shallow water. People who are afraid of water, but are interested in a water-exercise program, should be encouraged to take a basic learn-to-swim course in order to develop water adjustment skills prior to participating in an aqua fitness class.

B. Facility Check and Introductions

Before class, it is the responsibility of the instructor to:
- scan the pool and deck area for hazards, such as broken glass, debris, broken ladders, or slippery areas;
- correct or point out any dangerous situations, however minor, to participants;
- check the water temperature;
- make sure participants come to the workout warm and stay warm throughout (e.g., as participants arrive on the deck, encourage them to stay warm by wrapping up in a towel while waiting for class to begin, or ask them to get into the pool and to begin moving by walking or jogging.); and
- set up the music system away from the water's edge.

C. Attire

Special aquatic shoes should be worn to increase traction and ensure safety in and out of the pool. Instructors should wear swimsuits, and possibly tights as well, that provide adequate coverage. When participants look up from the pool at the instructor on the deck and watch as he/she climbs in and out of the pool for demonstrations, participants should not be distracted by the instructor's attire or lack thereof. A professional appearance allows more focus on learning.

D. Level of Participation

Check to be sure that all participants are comfortable in water and can recover to a stand if they lose their balance. Teach the intensity progression and sculling, and explain how to monitor intensity using perceived exertion and the talk test. Explain to participants that they must keep moving continuously to stay warm. Show them proper entrances, and identify the working area and depths. The recommendations for land-based exercise also apply.

E. Breathing

The same basic breathing principles on land apply for water as well. Encourage breathing, especially during "suspended" or deep-water exercise. When hydrostatic pressure of water pushes against the lungs, some participants will "top breathe," or perform shallow breaths, since it feels more difficult to inflate the lungs against pressure. Cue them to breathe.

F. Orientation to Water

Provide some brief tips on feeling buoyancy, finding a working depth, maintaining proper postural alignment in water, and monitoring intensity. Point out some differences between land and water, and explain how different the exercises will feel (e.g., cooler, lighter, speed varies the work). Simply using land-based movements in water may not optimize training. The properties of buoyancy and the resistance created by surface area, speed, and movement through water need to be taught. Advise participants that buoyancy will make them want to dance on their toes, and encourage them to practice pressing their heels to the bottom occasionally to avoid calf cramps, a common complaint from beginners.

IX. Additional Workout Tips

A. Special Considerations for Prenatal

The American College of Obstetricians and Gynecologists (ACOG) has written guidelines for exercise during pregnancy. Use these recommendations to coach participants who are pregnant in a water-fitness class. Here are a few tips to remember.

1. Women can continue to exercise and derive health benefits even from mild-to-moderate exercise routines.
2. Avoid cold water and/or airflow that may stimulate nipple erection and hormone changes.
3. Encourage participants to wear a sports bra under supportive swimwear for protection from chafing.
4. Protect softened connective tissue affected by relaxin by promoting muscle strength.
5. Limit the range of motion during hip-extension/-flexion moves to avoid stress on the broad and/or round ligaments.
6. Limit rebound moves and quick changes in direction.
7. Reinforce proper body alignment.
8. Vary the muscle groups to balance blood shunting and avoid fatigue.
9. Encourage hydration before, during, and after exercise bouts.

B. Questionable Exercises for the General Population

See AFAA's *Basic Exercise Standards and Guidelines*, section VI.B.

Exercises that should be considered for potential risk for the general population include the following.

1. Double leg raises while hanging backward on the pool wall (creates excessive pressure on the lumbar disks)
2. One leg on pool gutter with forward flexion for a hamstring stretch (may overload the lumbar spine and does not effectively stretch the targeted muscle; may also cause piriformis syndrome)
3. Full "crunches" with legs hooked over the pool gutter
4. Crossing legs midline of the body (for those who have had a hip replacement)
5. Full leg extensions after ACL knee surgery
6. Lifting weighted objects, like jugs filled with water, overhead while the body is partially submerged (compromises balance, dramatically increases blood pressure, and can impinge the shoulder joint)
7. Repetitive arm work above the surface of the water—stresses the shoulder joint and does not contribute significantly to cardiorespiratory conditioning. Studies show that arm-cranking moves, as well as arm work above the head, produce a higher heart rate rela

tive to VO_2 (oxygen consumption) demands. Resistive work with the arms produces relatively low oxygen uptake and does not meet the criteria for aerobic training intensity due to the pressor response. Above-water arm work should be limited and functional.

8. Adding land weights to a water workout—should be limited to physical therapy work only. There are many risks to be considered with this method of overload.

9. Wall lifts—lifting the body upward out of the water using the wall or pool gutter should be evaluated for individual safety. Maintaining proper body mechanics during this exercise is difficult for most people.

Evaluate the cost and benefits of each exercise. Any movement that compromises proper body alignment should be reevaluated. Remember to determine the direction of buoyancy and resistance acting against the body and examine the resulting contractions needed to maintain alignment. If an exercise can be done differently and more safely, modify it.

Keep in mind the following general recommendations for participants with back and/or shoulder problems. For participants suffering from back problems, decrease forward speed and stabilize the spine during travel moves. For participants with a history of shoulder dislocation, limit shoulder external rotation to 20° back (behind the body).

C. Monitoring Intensity in Water

Heart rates are difficult to assess accurately, even during land exercise. In water, assessing heart rate is even more difficult and seems to be less effective due to a wide number of variables, such as motivation, fitness level, water temperature, clothing worn by the participant, water depth, and exercise types. Lower heart rates in water may correlate with a cardiorespiratory training effect on land expected from a higher heart rate. It is recommended that participants use a combination of perceived exertion, the talk test, and heart rates (if they are highly skilled) to determine exercise intensity.

D. Music

1. Choose music that's fun and motivating. Instructors can use a variety of tempos, sounds, and styles to give a sense of excitement and energy. Remember, it takes individual effort to press through the resistance of water, and music can motivate. However, since intensity is regulated by speed, allow participants to work on their own beat, not the instructor's or the music's.

2. During muscular conditioning sets, the instructor may want to use a continuous-type tape with a pace of about 120–130 bpm to provide motivation and variety. The duration of the repetitions and sets can be changed according to the group's fitness level, not according to song length.

3. For aerobic conditioning classes, various 3–8-minute songs provide opportunities to change the type and mood of continuous exercise. For interval work, music can be faded in and out for timed work and rest sets. Spinning- or cycle-training music can provide selections that work well in water.

4. It is extremely difficult to provide safe and effective training for everyone while working to the music beat. Allow participants to enjoy the music, working at their own intensity and pace. As previously mentioned, different body types react differently in water. The participant's own force and speed provide a personal level of resistance for self-directed training.

E. Saunas and Hot Tubs

Saunas, hot tubs, and hot showers may be appropriate after water exercise when the body has chilled. Encourage participants to warm up if they feel chilled. Average pool water temperature and a wet body in cool air will make the body feel cool as the workout begins to slow down. Overheating the body should be avoided as well, so limit heat exposure after exercise.

F. Hydration

The principles of hydration apply the same in water as they do on land. Sometimes people think that because they are exercising in water, they don't need to drink water. Also, since heat stress is not as much of a problem in water, thirst may not be stimulated in the same way it is during land classes. Moisture is lost through sweat and respiration, and as these factors increase during water exercise, the body must be hydrated to avoid fatigue. Have participants bring water bottles and encourage them to drink periodically.

G. Exercise Design Considerations

1. Participants must be taught basic skills to be able to move safely and effectively through the water, such as how to use their hands to coordinate every move in water and provide stability. For the most effective training, hands should be used primarily to optimize the water's resistance and to support the body. Webbed gloves are highly recommended to provide a larger surface area that encour-

ages a slower speed of the hand through water and more effectively matches the slower speed of the lower body. Coordinating the larger, more buoyant moves will be easier when upper and lower body speeds are more closely matched. Additionally, webbed gloves provide more efficient sculling motions to assist with travel and balance, and offer a progressive overload for upper-body training.

2. Shoes should be worn during all shallow-water workouts to provide traction for maximal speed and protection.

3. Land-based movements do not necessarily optimize water training. Two training studies that used land-based moves, one on an aquatic step and the other during a rhythmic shallow-water program, showed no significant improvements in cardiorespiratory endurance. This contradicts results from other studies using water-specific movements that report significant gains in cardiorespiratory conditioning. These latter programs may have addressed the properties of water with their exercise design more effectively. Optimization of training results requires modification of land movements for water and the application of intensity progressions to provide individualized water-specific work.

4. Abdominals are trained in a functional vertical stance in water. Research supports vertical abdominal compression during dynamic postural alignment against the water's buoyancy as well as resistance to train the trunk muscles. This technique should be used constantly during class so abdominal isolation work is not needed. Cue participants to proper alignment and give corrective feedback for improvements.

8 STANDARDS and GUIDELINES for *Low-Impact Aerobics*

I. Introduction

Instructing a safe and effective low-impact aerobics (LIA) class that benefits everyone from the high-impact "die-hard" to the aerobic novice is a definite challenge for instructors. Clearly, there is now the advantage of many years of practical application and biomechanical expertise to draw from in order to design enjoyable and effective LIA classes. These guidelines are to be used in conjunction with AFAA's *Basic Exercise Standards and Guidelines*, which instructors should refer to when addressing fitness training recommendations, professional responsibilities and concerns, exercise evaluation, and class components.

II. Impact and Intensity

A. Low-Impact vs. High-Impact Aerobics

LIA is a form of exercise in which all of the movement patterns are performed with at least one foot in contact with the floor at all times. By keeping one foot grounded, the amount of stress associated with the floor impact is significantly lessened. Some common examples of LIA moves are marching, step touches, heel digs, grapevines, lift steps, and lunges.

LIA does not necessarily imply that the class is performed at low intensity. Because LIA has less impact, it is often perceived as lower intensity than it actually is. New participants are often surprised when they monitor their heart rates to learn that their heart rate is indeed within or above their target training heart rate ranges. The intensity varies from beginning to advanced levels, depending on exercise selection, exercise sequencing, and movement patterns. Indeed, there are many benefits for all fitness levels, from improved health to desired body composition changes.

By contrast, a high-impact class primarily contains movements in which one or both feet may leave the floor, such as jogging, hopping, skipping, and jumping. Both techniques are valid and effective depending upon individual needs and body types. Many participants prefer a combination of the two styles of impact. Today, this "combo" class is referred to as hi-lo cardio (aerobics). Hi-lo ranges from moderate to high intensity and includes balanced impact intensity forces. Biomechanically, hi-lo can be easier on the joints than a traditional high-impact class.

According to research performed by Drs. Peter and Lorna Francis of San Diego State University, the softer landings in LIA can reduce the vertical force on the ball of the foot to about 1 ½ times the weight of the body. This is a considerable improvement over the jumps and hops in a conventional high-impact class, which create a force that can exceed 3 times the weight of the body.

B. Is LIA Actually Safer?

The good news is that there is less pounding and fewer aches and pains associated with LIA than with high-impact aerobics. Research shows that by eliminating the impact of repetitive jumping, there is a reduction in the risk of stress on the articular surfaces of the joints and a decrease in the chance of tendon overuse injury or shin splints. The bad news is this kind of exercise program, like any other form of exercise, is not without its problems. If workouts are not choreographed and taught effectively, the muscular stress of low-impact movements may strain participants in some unexpected way (e.g., faulty choreography that requires a sudden change of direction can cause unexpected excessive torque to the knee).

III. Factors Influencing Intensity

In any aerobic exercise class, intensity (along with duration and frequency) is a key factor in cardiorespiratory endurance improvement. However, simply understanding the conditioning principles is not enough to teach an effective LIA class. Intensity will vary depending on the following factors: (a) exercise selection, (b) elevated movements, (c) sequencing, (d) speed, and (e) lever length. The instructor must understand how to manipulate the factors, particularly if very fit participants are going to be challenged.

- Exercise Selection

   The variety of movements used and the choice of appropriate exercise for an individual's fitness level will be a determining factor in raising or lowering exercise intensity as well as maintaining a consistent intensity level throughout the aerobic portion of the class.

   Moderate- to high-intensity low-impact moves require the body to be lifted and lowered vertically against gravity. The legs have 4–5 times the muscle mass as compared to the upper body. Arm patterns help to increase intensity, but the bottom line is that full range of motion and movement that includes the moderate to larger leg muscles is the best way to increase cardiorespiratory conditioning.

- Elevated Movements

   Intensity of a particular movement is also influenced by the elevation at which it is performed. For example, the intensity of performing bi-

ceps curls with the elbows raised out to the sides of the body at shoul
der height is greater than when the same movement is performed with
the elbows at waist level. This is because the gravitational pull is stron
ger when the body or limbs are in an extended, raised, or long-lever
position as compared to a short-lever, lower position.

- Sequencing
  The manner in which the movement patterns or variation of move
  ment patterns are added on, and/or combined and sequenced, is an
  other controlling factor of intensity in a low-impact class.

  Example #1
    1. March 1,2,3, knee lift in place 2 x (8 counts)
    2. Add on 4 alternating hamstring curls (8 counts)
    3. Combine #1 and #2 to make a 16-count combination
  Example #2
    1. Travel forward and backward
       March forward 1,2,3, knee lift (4 counts)
       March backward 1,2,3, knee lift (4 counts)
    2. Add on 4 alternating hamstring curls (8 counts)
    3. Combine #1 and #2 to make a 16-count combination

  The movement patterns in examples #1 and #2 are the same, but the
  intensity levels are different. If the instructor sequenced the examples
  in reverse, the intensity of the workout would be the opposite. It is crit
  ical for the instructor to pay attention to the sequencing of movement
  patterns in order to achieve the desired intensity levels.

- Speed
  Speed of movement during a low-impact class will have a direct effect
  on elevation of heart rate. Movement either in place or in traveling
  patterns across the floor should be performed through a full range of
  motion with control. Determine if the speed of movement across the
  floor is correct by noting if momentum and alignment are controlled.

- Lever Length
  Arm or leg exercises that use extended levers (e.g., straight arms in a
  horizontal position as opposed to bent elbows in the same position)
  will increase the workload or intensity of the movement due to the
  amount of force required to move the lever—in this case, an arm
  against gravity. It is also more difficult to control movement without
  momentum through a full range of motion and maintain proper body
  alignment with the use of longer levers. Long-lever movements should
  be modified for beginners or interspersed with short-lever movements
  in sequencing patterns as a means of controlling intensity.

V. Summary

LIA is suited for virtually every healthy individual if instructed and performed safely according to recommended training principles. It is an ideal activity for those who must restrict stress to the knees, feet, lower legs, and hips. Although LIA was not developed to replace high-impact aerobics, its popularity has continued to grow over the years. A more recent industry trend has been to combine both high-impact and low-impact aerobics into what is commonly referred to as the hi-lo cardio workout.

9

STANDARDS and GUIDELINES for
Group Resistance Training (GRT)

I. Introduction

Resistance training performed within the group exercise setting continues to be a popular trend among fitness professionals. Resistance training involves working individual or groups of muscles against a resistance to the point of muscle fatigue. Different forms of resistance can be used, such as dumbbells, weighted bars and balls, resistance tubes, or body weight. Sample workouts include calisthenics/floor work, body sculpting, or circuit training. These guidelines were developed to be used in conjunction with AFAA's *Basic Exercise Standards and Guidelines*, and apply to an average adult without known physiological or biological conditions that would in any way restrict his/her exercise activities.

II. Basic Principles, Definitions, and Recommendations

A. Terminology

1. **Constant Resistance**

   Constant resistance is a form of dynamic resistance where the resistance directed against the target muscle or muscle group does not vary through the range of motion. Constant resistance training uses free weights, such as dumbbells, barbells, medicine balls, or even your own body weight. Gravity and position play a major role in the effectiveness of this type of resistance. The main disadvantage of constant resistance is the inability to train effectively against gravity through a full range of motion for certain exercises.

2. **Variable Resistance**

   Variable resistance exercise is designed to achieve maximum muscular involvement, and is usually carried out through the use of specialized machines. When using variable resistance machines, the applied force changes throughout the range of motion due to the special arrangement of pulleys or cams. With variable resistance machines, the resistance design attempts to match the particular muscle's strength curve, allowing for a fuller range of effective training. True variable resistance is hard to duplicate in a group exercise class. The closest thing to variable resistance that is used in a group class would be elastic tubing and bands. Unlike a fixed weight, elastic resistance is variable because the resistance continues to increase as the device is progressively stretched, compressed, bent, or twisted.

3. **Progressive Resistance Exercise**

   Progressive resistance exercise is the basis for all weight training programs, and is the practical application of the overload principle. For continued improvements in fitness, an exercise program should provide gradual increases or progressions. Proper progression includes a systematic change in training volume over time, designed to maximize fitness gains while keeping the risk of overtraining and related injuries low. For program progressions, allow for the initial conditioning phase to last 4–6 weeks, improvement phase 4–5 months, and maintenance thereafter. Recommended progressions will vary depending on the participant's age, physical limitations, and fitness level. Resistance training programs can be progressed in a number of ways, including varying the reps, sets, weight, rest period between sets, speed, type of equipment used (e.g., dumbbells, barbells, elastic bands, medicine balls, stability balls, foam rollers), and the type of exercise.

4. **Circuit Training**

   Circuit training involves timed bouts of activities/exercises performed in a station-to-station, or sequential, manner. A class can perform a circuit in a stationary position with all participants performing the same activity simultaneously, or with participants moving around the room from station to station performing different exercises. These activities can be designed to improve cardiorespiratory endurance, muscular strength, or a combination of both.

5. **Muscle Balancing**

   Muscle balancing is a foundational concept for resistance training workouts. All the muscles of the body work in pairs to create movement. If one part of the pair is stronger than another, a muscular imbalance is created, which leads to improper body alignment and movement mechanics.

6. **Joint Actions**

   (These definitions assume that movement takes place from the anatomical position.)
   - Flexion—movement that shortens the angle between two bones. Flexion moves anteriorly (forward) parallel to the median plane, with the exception of knee flexion.
   - Extension—movement that increases the angle between two bones. Extension moves posteriorly (back) parallel to the median plane, with the exception of knee extension.
   - Lateral Spinal Flexion—bending of the spine to the side

- Adduction—movement toward the midline of the body
- Abduction—movement away from the midline of the body
- Horizontal flexion/horizontal adduction—movement towar the midline of the body in the horizontal plane
- Horizontal extension/horizontal abduction—movement awa from the midline of the body in the horizontal plane
- Rotation—medial or lateral movement around an axis
- Circumduction—movement in which an extremity describes 360° circle
- Supination—the lateral rotation of the forearm, bringing th palm of the hand upward. In this position, the radius and uln are parallel.
- Pronation—medial rotation of the forearm, with the palm in downward position so the radius lies diagonally across the uln
- Eversion—rotation of the foot with the sole turned outwar (sometimes referred to as pronation)
- Inversion—rotation of the foot with the sole turned inwar (sometimes referred to as supination)
- Dorsiflexion—movement that brings the top of the foot towar the shin
- Plantarflexion—movement that brings the sole of the foo downward (pointing the toes)
- Depression—downward movement of the shoulder girdle
- Elevation—upward movement of the shoulder girdle
- Scapular adduction (also known as retraction)—backwar movement of the shoulder girdle with scapulae pulled towar the midline
- Scapular abduction (also known as protraction)—forwar movement of the shoulder girdle with scapulae pulled awa from the midline
- Scapular upward rotation—rotation (or upward turning) of th scapula in the frontal plane with the glenoid fossa facing upwar
- Scapular downward rotation—return from upward rotation
- Scapular upward tilt—a turning of the scapula on its fron tal-horizontal axis so that the superior border turns slightl forward-downward and the inferior border moves slightl backward-upward (and away from the rib cage)
- Reduction of upward tilt—return movement from upward tilt

- Line of pull—the direction of the muscle from its origin to its insertion. The line of pull across a joint will determine the function(s) of the muscle.

7. **Planes**
    - Planes geometrically bisect the body and describe bodily movements. (Movements take place alongside or next to the planes.) There are an infinite number of parallel planes to each plane listed below.
    - Horizontal plane—(sometimes called transverse) divides the body into upper and lower portions. Rotation occurs within the horizontal plane.
    - Frontal plane—(sometimes called the coronal) divides the body into front and back. Abduction and adduction occur within the frontal plane.
    - Sagittal—(occasionally called the medial) divides the body into right and left portions. Flexion and extension occur within the sagittal plane.

8. **Positions and Directional Terms**
    - Anterior—to the front
    - Posterior—to the back
    - Lateral—away from the midline
    - Medial—toward the midline
    - Superior—above
    - Inferior—below
    - Superficial—on or near the surface of the body
    - Deep—further from the surface of the body
    - Proximal—closer to the trunk
    - Distal—further from the trunk
    - Supine—lying on the spine (on the back)
    - Prone—lying face down

9. **Joint Movers**
    - Agonist—prime mover, or the contracting muscle that is responsible for the movement exhibited
    - Antagonist—the muscle that works in opposition to the prime mover and reflexively elongates to allow the agonist to contract and move the joint
    - Assistor—the muscle that assists in performing a movement, but is not a prime mover (sometimes called a secondary mover)
    - Stabilizer—the muscle that maintains a static or isometric contraction to anchor or support the movement of the primary mover

• Synergist—textbooks disagree on the definition of a synergist. Some describe it as a stabilizer; some describe it as an assistor. The muscle is contracting synergistically along with the prime mover in some way.

10. **Muscle Contractions (Actions)**

When muscles "work," or develop force or tension, they are said to contract. However, this implies that the muscles shorten. Muscles sometimes shorten when they work, but they can also lengthen or even stay the same length and still produce tension. There are three main types of muscle actions.

• Isometric—a held, static muscle action where there is no change in the joint angle or muscle length. Strength gains that result from isometric contractions are joint-angle specific. A disadvantage of an isometric contraction is the tendency for breath holding (Valsalva maneuver), leading to a rise in blood pressure, which can be quite dangerous.

• Concentric—shortening action of a muscle as it develops tension against a resistance (often called a positive contraction)

• Eccentric—lengthening action of a muscle as it develops tension against a resistance (often called a negative contraction)

11. **Muscle and Joint Attachments**

• Ligament—band of fibrous tissue that connects bone to bone and provides joint stability. Ligaments are non-elastic; once stretched, they remain stretched.

• Tendon—dense, fibrous connective tissue that forms the end of a muscle and attaches the muscle to bone

• Fascia—fibrous connective tissue that forms sheaths for individual muscles

• Cartilage—white, semi-opaque, fibrous connective tissue that cushions the joints and prevents wear on articular (joint) surfaces

• Synovial membrane—a thin tissue surrounding most movable joints that secretes synovial fluid. This fluid provides nourishment, lubrication, and hydrostatic cushioning.

• Bursae—liquid-filled membranes that protect soft tissues as they pass by bony projections

12. Muscle Terminology
- Smooth muscle—a type of muscle tissue that is present in many organs (e.g., intestines), and is generally not under voluntary control
- Cardiac muscle—an entire structure of interconnected cardiac fibers that contracts involuntarily as a unit
- Skeletal muscle (striated muscle)—muscle tissue that causes joint movement and is under voluntary control. Skeletal muscles can have several types of fiber arrangements.
  - Fusiform muscle—fibers are arranged parallel to the line of pull, usually in a spindle shape, tapering at each end (e.g., biceps brachialis)
  - Longitudinal muscle—a long strap-like muscle with parallel fibers (e.g., rectus abdominus)
  - Fan-shaped or triangular muscle—a flat muscle whose fibers radiate from a narrow end to a broad end (e.g., pectoralis major)
  - Pennate muscle—densely packed muscle fibers are arranged oblique to the line of pull in a feather-like arrangement. May be unipennate (e.g., tibialis posterior), bipennate (e.g., rectus femoris), or multipennate (e.g., deltoid).

B. Precautions

See AFAA's *Basic Exercise Standards and Guidelines*, section V.A.5.

Weights are used in group exercise programs to provide resistance for muscular strengthening and muscle endurance training. Healthy individuals without a known history of joint injury or cardiovascular, metabolic, or pulmonary disease may safely participate in a group resistance training (GRT) workout. However, persons with known joint injury or cardiovascular, metabolic, or pulmonary disease should not participate in a GRT workout without a physician's written release. The increased peripheral vascular resistance that can occur with weights causes an increase in both systolic and diastolic blood pressure. In addition, participants who have musculoskeletal limitations, joint injuries, muscle strains, tendinitis, bursitis, ligamentitis, or other orthopedic limitations must also provide a written release from their physician prior to participation.

C. When To Use Group Exercise Resistance Training Equipment

1. For upper and lower body strengthening exercises in a stationary position

2. During circuit workouts that include cardio and strength pattern in alternating bouts or integrated patterns with controlled range and movement speeds

D. When Not To Use Group Exercise Resistance Training Equipment

1. While performing fast and/or long-lever movements that rely on force or momentum to complete the full range of motion

2. On an injured or compromised limb unless exercise is specifically performed for rehabilitative purposes under a physician's supervision

3. Avoid heavy loads (weights) and/or excessive repetitions during the warm-up

4. While performing the cool-down

E. Types of Equipment

1. Dumbbells or stick-type (e.g., body bar)

2. Wraparound weights—used on ankles or wrists and secured by Velcro straps

3. Weighted gloves— contain weights in pockets on back and/or in palm of hand

4. Kettlebells®—cast iron weights looking somewhat like a cannonball with a handle

5. Medicine balls—weighted balls that are roughly 4–12 inches in width and range in weight from 2–20 lb

6. Resistance tubing and bands—rubber tubing with handles or elastic bands without handles (e.g., Thera-band®)

III. Training Principles and Guidelines

See AFAA's *Basic Exercise Standards and Guidelines*, section VIII.D.

A. Frequency

1. GRT workouts are performed in a variety of combinations and formats. The frequency of the workout is based on the type of class. All workouts should be of sufficient frequency to maintain or improve fitness levels, yet avoid potential risk of overuse.

2. The number of days spent specifically training for strength is dependent upon the intensity of the workout performed. Training with body weight or light workloads for either upper or lower body can be performed without a need for a recovery day. When training with heavier loads, it will be important to allow for proper recovery by maintaining non-consecutive workout days or by alternating muscle groups worked. For example, train upper body 2 days per week and lower body 2 days per week. In addition to alternating body parts, instructor's can also vary the exercise selection and equipment used to create heavy and light workout days (e.g., weights vs. bands).

3. Rest is an important variable in determining the success of any resistance training program. During exercise, muscle fibers can be heavily stressed, resulting in microscopic damage. It is between exercise sessions that the repair process takes place and muscle fibers actually become stronger. Inadequate rest can result in over-trained, weakened muscles. The amount of rest needed is relative to the intensity of the work performed.

B. Intensity

See AFAA's *Basic Exercise Standards and Guidelines*, section VIII.D.3.

In order to see the results from a strength program, it is important to work the targeted muscle group to fatigue, but not to a point of failure. This means the muscle feels tired, but you are able to complete the movement without the loss of proper exercise form and technique. The specific exercise, load, repetitions, and sets used will affect the intensity and training effect of a workout.

1. Amount of Resistance (or Load)

- The amount of the resistance being used is dependant upon the fitness levels of the participants, reps and sets performed, exercise selection, and program goals.
- Class formats that are focusing on stationary strength exercises can use light and heavier loads depending on what is available in the group environment (typically ranging from 1–50 pounds [lb]).
- Class formats that combine cardio movement with hand-held weights will need to adjust the amount of resistance to allow for proper range of motion and movement control. This type of workout will need to use lighter loads (typically ranging from 1–10 lb).

2. Number of Reps and Sets

- The number of reps and sets is dependent upon fitness levels, weight load, exercise selection, and program goals.
- As the amount of overload or resistance increases, decrease reps and sets, building up again slowly.
  - For **muscular endurance**, use workloads that allow you to correctly perform a higher number of repetitions (greater than 15) and/or sets with minimal breaks between sets. Multiples of 8 work best with music-driven workouts (e.g., 16, 24). As reps increase beyond 25, the time it takes to complete the exercise begins to mimic the overload definition for cardiorespiratory conditioning (continuous movement) and is usually ineffective in promoting further muscular endurance gains. This statement does not imply that significant cardiorespiratory conditioning takes place with high-repetition resistance training schemes. Research shows that the load generally does not engage enough muscle mass to generate a significant cardiorespiratory training effect (Fleck & Kraemer, 2004). More importantly, high repetitions may lead to overuse injuries, contributing to poor outcomes and the associated risk of frustration and decreased adherence (Powers & Howley, 2009).
  - For **muscular strength**, use workloads that allow you to feel muscular fatigue in 15 or less repetitions (ideally 8–12). A 1 repetition maximum (1RM) is a standard by which muscular strength is measured. It is the maximum amount of resistance lifted through the range of motion for one repetition of a given exercise (with correct form and execution). Once the maximum volume is determined, a person can calculate a recommended training volume by using 60–80% of the maximum volume lifted (1RM). The percentage used depends on fitness level and limitations. Note that 1RM testing is not recommended for the average participant due to the intimidation factor and risks inherent to any type of maximal test, thus the proper workload will need to be determined by trial and error.
  - Progression should occur as a 5% increase as the participant reaches the 12-rep goal. In other words, when the execution of 12 reps at a given weight becomes easy, increase the weight by approximately 5% for future sets. As the workload or resistance increases, decrease reps and sets, building up again slowly. An individual should not

increase the amount of weight or resistance until she/he can properly perform two sets of 8–12 repetitions in the same range of motion without fatiguing the muscle(s).

– Since working with very heavy weights is generally not an option in the group exercise setting, isometric holds and short-range pulses are additional techniques used in resistance classes to expedite the onset of muscle fatigue. These holds and small pulsing reps are typically added after the final set of full-range repetitions, in particular, when the resistance available does not sufficiently fatigue the muscle in the recommended rep ranges.

3. Type

- Changing the mode, type, or variation of an exercise can help increase intensity.

  For example, moving from an isolation exercise (e.g., a standing biceps curl) to a compound exercise (e.g., alternating front lunges performed simultaneously with biceps curls) is another way to increase the intensity and metabolic challenge.

C. Duration

Muscle strengthening should include sufficient time to overload muscle/muscle groups to produce a training effect. The duration of a workout is dependent upon the amount of weight, exercise selection, and number of repetitions per exercise.

1. A full body group exercise resistance training class generally lasts 1 hour.

2. Combination workouts are also offered in which 20–30 minutes are allotted for cardio activity and 20–30 minutes towards muscular strength and endurance exercises.

3. Time in training can also refer to the time spent during each repetition and rest period between sets of repetitions. To achieve maximum effectiveness during resistance exercises, it is important to control the amount of tension during both the concentric and eccentric phase of a movement. This type of "consciously applied resistance" is only possible if movements are performed in a controlled manner at a slow to moderate pace.

   - It is recommended to use 4–8 seconds per repetition (concentric and eccentric phase) when performing full-range movement (typically 8–16 beats of music). Shorter repetition time frames can be used during partial-range or short-range pulses. Thus, if performing 8–16 repetitions, at a 4-second per rep

tempo, each set would last somewhere between 32 seconds an
a full minute.

- Once fatigue is reached, it is time to rest prior to performin
another set of the same exercise. Rest periods between sets (
an exercise can range from a minimum of a few seconds to
few minutes. The heavier the load and greater the fatigue, th
longer the rest periods between sets should last. Shorter re
periods can be used if working with lighter loads.

- Rest periods can be minimized or omitted if alternating se
between muscle groups using super-sets, tri-sets, and giant se
(i.e., a combination of two, three, or more different exercise
done back to back without a rest period). This technique
often used during resistance classes to avoid long rest perioc
and keep the flow of the workout going.

Summary FITT Guidelines—Group Resistance Training

F = 2–3 days per week (more if using sub-maximal loads)

I = To the point of muscle fatigue while maintaining proper
form; typically 8–25 repetitions, 1–4 sets, depending if focus is
strength or endurance.

T = 20–60 minutes (time to complete 1–4 sets of one exercise for
each major muscle group)

T = Progressive static and dynamic forms of resistance training
including at least one exercise for each major muscle group,
utilizing both single-joint and multi-joint, multi-muscle
exercises (e.g., progressive weight training, calisthenics, elastic
tubing).

D. Overload

A training effect will occur when a muscle is regularly overloaded be
yond the level to which it is accustomed to working. Overload is accom
plished by increasing any one or a combination of the following factor:
(a) amount of weight, (b) reps, and (c) sets.

1. During resistance training, overload is best achieved by progres
sively increasing the amount of weight or the number of reps an
sets per muscle group as the workload becomes easier. The trainin
method of overload used is dependent upon training goals (e.g.
muscle strength vs. muscle endurance [hypertrophy vs. tone]).

2. Performing a high number of repetitions with low weight will in
crease muscle endurance and definition. Performing a small num
ber of repetitions with heavier weight will enhance muscle fibe
hypertrophy and increase strength.

E. Resistance

Whether one is working with or without the added resistance of weights, muscle strengthening occurs when a muscle or group of muscles is worked against a resistance. To achieve maximum effectiveness, resistance is accomplished not only by the use of weights, but by controlling the amount of tension during both the concentric and eccentric phase of a movement. Recruitment of muscle fiber is increased as a muscle and/or muscle group becomes "trained," increasing the amount of tension or force that the muscle(s) must work against. This type of "consciously applied resistance" is only possible if movements are performed in a controlled manner at a slow to moderate pace.

F. Isolation and Specificity

When training with weights, it is important to follow these steps.

1. Identify personal goals and the focus of each exercise.

   Although each participant's exercise goals are unique, many people wish to enhance muscle strength and muscle endurance, as well as increase their core stability. A thorough resistance training program should address all of these goals. Below is a general summary of the three primary resistance training goals, and how to achieve them in a resistance training class.

   a. **Goal 1: Muscle Endurance**
   - The ability of a muscle or group of muscles to repeatedly contract against resistance over an extended period of time
   - 16–25 repetitions of sub-maximal force
   - Loads less than 65% 1RM
   - Minimum recovery periods required between sets

   Endurance training allows participants to establish a neuromuscular relationship to the routine, proper training techniques, and effort perception.

   b. **Goal 2: Muscle Strength**
   - The ability of a muscle or group of muscles to exert force against a resistance
   - 8–12 repetitions of a near-maximal force
   - Training load between 60% and 80% 1RM
   - Longer recovery periods required between sets

   Strength training is designed to increase force production and encourage muscle hypertrophy.

   c. **Goal 3: Muscle Stability**
   - The ability to control joint alignment and performance in space against gravity and unexpected or unstable forces

- The core musculature of the body plays a large role in this type of training focus
- Reduce workloads at first
- Training from less stable positions or on less stable surfaces, such as balance training devices, are an ideal way to illicit and progress these demands

    Stability training is designed to take one's strength and make it more usable/functional by enhancing stability and muscular reaction time.

2. Identify the muscle or muscle groups being strengthened.
3. Choose exercises that will specifically isolate and work the muscle that are the focus of the workout goals.
4. Remember to work the opposing muscle(s) to avoid muscular imbalance.

G. Exercise Danger Signs When Using Low Weights and Other General Precautions

Know the exercise danger signs outlined in AFAA's *Basic Exercise Standards and Guidelines*, section V.B. In addition, be aware of the following conditions and considerations, and understand their relationship to the added physiological stresses of working with weights.

- Momentum—never let a weight build up momentum because the risk of joint and muscle injury is increased.
- Breathing and the Valsalva maneuver
- Effect of lever length on joint stress
- Hyperextension of the joints—tendency to hyperextend increases with weighted exercise; limb and joint injury occurs with hyperextension along with weakening of ligaments, tendons, and connective tissue.
- Too much weight/inappropriate weight for activity—overstresses muscles and joints.

H. Posture and Alignment

See AFAA's *Basic Exercise Standards and Guidelines*, section VI. In addition, be aware of the danger of hyperextending joints, and the added joint and ligament stress of weighted workouts.

I. Breathing

Breathing rhythmically throughout exercise is essential to preventing blood pressure and heart rate elevation. Exhaling on the exertion will help prevent over-elevation.

IV. Class Formats

See AFAA's *Basic Exercise Standards and Guidelines*, section VII.

A. Progressive Resistance—Reps and Sets Format

Progressive resistance training is the foundation of all strength training workouts. The goal of a progressive resistance class format is to encourage participants to reach appropriate levels of muscular fatigue within a reasonable time frame and sensible series of reps and sets. Participants should be encouraged to gradually increase workloads over a period of time as their muscles become progressively stronger. This can be accomplished through the use of heavier loads, more challenging exercise variations, and/or creative sequencing. This is the most effective way of enhancing muscular strength. In a group exercise class, we typically refer to the resistance as light or heavy. Although this is muscle and ability specific, for the purpose of teaching group exercise, light or low weight refers to exercising with a load that produces minimal to moderate fatigue levels (endurance training levels) in 8–16 reps (typically 1–10 lb). Heavy weight would include classes that utilize weights or a load that produces a high level of muscle fatigue (strength training levels) within 8–16 repetitions. These classes target all of the major muscle groups through a combination of isolation and multi-joint, multi-muscle exercises.

B. Circuit Training Format

Circuit training involves timed bouts of strength and/or cardio activity. It is a format generally utilized to increase metabolic activity levels while performing strength training exercises. Upper and lower extremities are alternated in a sequential manner for a designated time. This allows for shorter rest periods between exercises, and results in higher metabolic activity levels and training heart rates. Between 8–15 exercise stations are commonly used. Participants may move from station to station or perform the various exercises from a single station (sometimes referred to as a unison circuit). Some circuit workouts include cardiorespiratory equipment and exercises (e.g., steps and jump ropes) alternated with resistance training stations and exercises. A workout in which cardio segments are alternated with resistance training segments is sometimes called a super-circuit. Circuits may also be designed around sports-specific goals. This is accomplished by including exercises that relate to the specific demands of a particular sporting activity (e.g., isometric wall squats in a ski fitness circuit). A circuit is typically repeated two to three times to equal 20–45 minutes of continuous exercise.

C. Cardio/Strength Integrated Format

Cardio/strength integrated training merges upper and lower body movements with the goal of working both the cardiorespiratory system and the musculoskeletal system simultaneously. Examples would be light-weight, low-impact, or step routines where basic foot patterns are performed at the same time as controlled upper body strength exercises (e.g., a basic step with a biceps curl). Additional guidelines should be followed when integrating movements. During the execution of integrated patterns the weight load, movement pace, and range of motion must allow for core stability as well as proper execution of both the foot and upper body movements. These workouts may not be appropriate for participants with poor body control and coordination. Care must be taken not to overtax the shoulder joint.

D. Combination Format

Many class formats include a combination of cardiorespiratory, strength, and flexibility exercises performed within the class for a total body workout. An example would be a 1-hour class that includes 20 minutes of step, cycle, or dance-based movement; 20 minutes of resistance training; and 20 minutes of preparatory and post-exercise stretching.

V. Pre-Class Announcements

See AFAA's *Basic Exercise Standards and Guidelines*, section VIII.A.
   All resistance training workouts will include three components.

A. The Warm-Up

1. Resistance training classes should start with an appropriate warm-up lasting from 5–10 minutes.
2. The warm-up may include non-weighted or light-weighted strength moves, such as squats, lunges, shoulder shrugs, presses, and pulls.
3. The movement patterns used in the warm-up are preparing the body for the exercises that will be used later.
4. Exercises should not be performed to a point where one senses local muscle fatigue.
5. Mild stretches are optional and should only be held for short periods of time after warming the tissues.

B. Conditioning Phase (The Workout)

The purpose will depend on the class format and training goals (e.g., progressive resistance training, circuit training, integrated training, combination training). It includes everything between the warm-up and final phase lasting approximately 20–40 minutes.

C. Final Phase

The purpose of this section of class is to relax and work on increasing flexibility. Here is where you would add in static stretches to address the tight areas of the body as well as stretches for the muscle groups that were worked during the conditioning phase. It is also a time for final class announcements and/or positive affirmations (approximate time allotment, 5–10 minutes).

VII. Exercise Sequence and Training Design

When designing a group resistance training workout, instructors will need to consider the order or sequence in which they will perform each exercise. The exercise sequence used will define the content or training design of the class. A well-thought-out training design will ensure a balanced, effective, and engaging workout session. There are many design options depending on the class format, equipment available, and the focus of the workout. Shifting the exercise sequence and class design on a regular basis will keep the workout interesting as well as help to prevent training plateaus. Some of the many sequence examples include the following.

1. **Single- and multi-set design**: moving from one primary muscle group to the next (non-specific order), while performing 1–3 sets of 8–16 repetitions (reps)
2. **Super/bi-, tri-, and giant set training systems**: the execution of one set of an exercise directly followed by a different exercise set without a rest.
   - super/bi-set: two different exercises performed one after the other
   - tri-set: three different exercises performed one after the other
   - giant set: four or more different exercises performed one after the other
3. **Priority training system**: prioritizes the weaker muscles by working them first when energy levels are high (e.g., working the external rotators before the larger shoulder girdle and chest muscles)
4. **Position design**: utilizes the position of the body during the sequencing of exercises (e.g., standing vs. supine). With the exception of a circuit format, classes will flow more smoothly if you complete exercises in one position before moving on to another.
5. **Pre-exhaustion system**: targets stronger muscles by isolating them prior to performing exercises that work additional muscles simultaneously. An example would be to perform flys, which isolate the

strong pectoralis major, followed by bench presses, which add i
the smaller triceps muscles.

6. **Functional, multi-joint, and/or sports-specific training pattern**
involves designing a class around exercise sequences that includ
a higher focus on core training techniques, sports-specific move
ments, and activities of daily life

7. **Alternation of opposing muscle groups**: the alternation of exer
cises that work opposing muscle groups, such as pull versus pus
exercises. An example would be to do a bent-over horizontal rov
(pull exercise) followed by a push-up or chest press (push exer
cise). This method will promote muscle balancing.

8. **Alternation of upper body exercises with lower body exercise**
the alternation of exercises for the upper and lower body, suc
as performing a set of overhead presses for the upper back an
shoulders followed by squats for the hips and legs. Other example
would include (a) biceps curls followed by calf raises, and (b) bent
over rows followed by side steps with a band around the ankles fo
hip abductors.

- **Pyramiding workloads**: involves changing the workloa
in relationship to the repetitions of an exercise performec
This can only be done if a variety of loads are available fo
each participant in class. For example, an ascending pyrami
would perform the first set of an exercise using lighter weigh
and then higher reps, gradually increasing the weight per se
while decreasing the reps. A descending pyramid would do th
reverse, start heavy with low reps and then decrease the weigh
while performing more reps.

- **Combined and integrated exercises**: combines or integrate
one exercise or movement with another. These sequence
include arm combinations, leg combinations, or arm and le
combinations.

  - **Arm combinations**—2 or more arm movements or move
    ment variations (e.g., biceps curl into an overhead press)
  - **Leg combinations**—2 or more leg movements or move
    ment variations (e.g., a front lunge into a hip hinge/rea
    leg extension)
  - **Arm and leg combinations**—2 or more arm and le
    movements or movement variations (e.g., squat to bicep
    curl; squat and curl simultaneously). This sequence i
    often used to boost the metabolic effect of a workout.

VII. Sample Methodology for GRT

Warm-Up

Warm-Up: 5–10 minutes

After some general limbering movements (e.g., reaches, shoulder rolls, posture reinforcement movements), mimic moves to be used in the workout (non-weighted). Combining the moves will help elevate the core temperature. For example:

- overhead press with leg abduction.
- alternating forward step-out lunge with front reach to row.
- calf raise to squat (hands to thighs) to back stretch.
- lateral raise with alternating side step-out lunge.

Optional preparatory stretches targeting typically tight muscle groups. For example:

- standing chest stretch hands behind hips (after the calf raise series).
- standing hip flexor stretch from lunge position transition to standing hamstring stretch (after the front lunge series).

(See AFAA's *Basic Exercise Standards & Guidelines*, section VIII.B.2.)

Toward the end of the warm-up, pick a move to establish the musical beat pattern to be used in the workout, such as biceps curls, triceps kickback, or standing scapular retraction (if using scapular retraction to teach the pattern, feel free to pick up weights).

4 beats(c) /4 beats(e)

2 beats(c) /6 beats(e)

6 beats(c) /2 beats(e)

8 beats(c) /8 beats(e)

The Workout

Class Format: Progressive Resistance Training: Reps and Sets

Equipment: 2 sets of dumbbells (a lighter set for smaller muscle groups and a heavier set for stronger muscle groups); step platform

Training Design: Upper Body/Lower Body Alternation

Super-Set Exercises—1 & 2, 3 & 4, 5 & 6, 7 & 8, 9 & 10, 11 & 12, 13 & 14

Design Goal: Increase training metabolism and reduce need for set breaks

Exercises—Target Muscle(s) and Exercise Sequence:
1. Standing Overhead Press (deltoids and triceps)
2. Squats (quadriceps, hamstrings, gluteals)
3. Bent-Over Horizontal Row (mid-trapezius, rhomboids, posterior deltoids, biceps)
4. Lunges (quadriceps, hamstrings, gluteals)
5. Lateral Deltoid Raise (deltoids)
6. Standing Calf Raise with Biceps Curl (gastrocnemius, soleus, biceps)

(The following exercises are performed on the step platform.)
7. Hip Lifts hips off step end (gluteals, hamstrings)
8. Chest Press (pectoralis major, anterior deltoids, triceps)
9. Abdominal Crunches with Ankle Dorsiflexion (abdominals, anterior tibialis)
10. Reverse Curls (abdominals and obliques)
11. Supine Triceps Extension (triceps)
12. Supine Alternating Leg Reach and Hold (core stabilization exercise)
13. Back Extension (erector spinae)
14. Prone Alternating Leg Extensions (gluteals)

Reps/Sets and Training Time: 16 to 20 reps/2 sets
   1 min per set (x 2 sets) = 2 min per exercise (x 14 exercises) = 28 min total
   1 min per exercise for set-up and breaks between sets (x 14 exercises) = 14 min total
Total Conditioning Phase = 42 minutes

Musical Beat Pattern *(optional)*

Approximately 1 minute per set
   Reps 1 to 8: 4 beats (c) /4 beats (e)=(64 total beats) slow up/slow down
   Reps 9 to 12: 2 beats (c) /6 beats (e)=(32 total beats) quick up/slow down
   Reps 13 to 16: 6 beats (c) /2 beats (e)=(32 total beats) slow up/quick down
*Ideally, you should start each set at the top of the musical phrase (32 counts).

Set Break or Rep On: Approximately 30 seconds (will depend on loads used)

   Reps 17 to 20: 8 beats (c) /8 beats (e)=(64 total beats) super slow

   (c) = concentric phase of contraction (e) = eccentric phase of contraction

Flexibility Training

Post-Exercise Stretch: 5–10 minutes

Longer held (≥ 20 seconds) static stretches should be performed after exercising your muscle groups. This can be done in between exercises as an extended set break or at the final phase of the class once all exercises have been completed. If stretching between exercises, wait until all sets of a particular muscle group are finished prior to including the stretch break. This time will need to be factored into the overall workout time.

Final Phase: Suggested Stretches

Seated Pectoralis Stretch—hands behind head

Seated Deltoid/Mid-Trap Stretch—arm across chest (switch arms)

Seated Upper Trap/Neck Stretch—arm crosses behind body with head tilt (switch arms)

Seated Lateral Spinal Flexion—hand support on step platform (switch side)

Seated Spinal Rotation (switch side)

Seated Spinal Flexion (hands under thighs)

Seated Hamstring Stretch—one leg front (switch legs)

Standing Quad and Hip Flexor Stretch—lunge position (switch side)

Standing Quad Stretch and Balance—single leg up held behind body (switch leg)

10 STANDARDS and GUIDELINES for for Cardio Kickboxing

I. Introduction

There are a variety of ways to design kickboxing classes. These cardi kickboxing guidelines address formats and safety procedures, as well a the fundamental concept of modifications. When a competitive sport o exercise is brought into the group exercise forum, modifications need t be made to ensure that the exercise is as safe as possible and still effective a training the body. Professional boxers and kick boxers are willing to tak risks with their bodies in order to beat their opponent. They are also mor highly trained than the exerciser in a group exercise setting. As a fitnes instructor, it is important to know the participants' fitness levels and to tr to prescreen participants when possible. Kickboxing instructors are chal lenged to clearly understand the exercise modifications necessary to mak their classes as safe as possible for all participants. In developing cardi kickboxing classes, use these guidelines in conjunction with AFAA's *Basi Exercise Standards and Guidelines*.

II. Exercise Evaluation Using the AFAA 5 Questions™

Because there are a variety of movements, styles, and disciplines bein introduced into the kickboxing class by instructors new to group exercise the AFAA 5 Questions™ can be useful in screening movements prior t introduction to the group setting. For kickboxing, special attention shoul be paid to questions #3 and #5.

1. What is the purpose of this exercise?
   Consider: muscular strength or endurance, cardiorespirator conditioning, flexibility, warm-up or activity preparation, ski development, and stress reduction

2. Are you doing that effectively?
   Consider: proper range, speed, or body position against gravity

3. Does the exercise create any safety concerns?
   Consider: potential stress areas, environmental concerns, or move ment control

4. Can you maintain proper alignment and form for the duration o the exercise?
   Consider: form, alignment, or stabilization

5. For whom is the exercise appropriate or inappropriate?
   Consider: risk-to-benefit ratio; whether the participant is at beginner, intermediate, or advanced level of fitness; and an limitations reported by the participant

Question 3 is extremely important when screening a movement taken from competitive boxing, kickboxing, or the martial arts. Keep in mind that the purpose of these sports is self-defense or beating an opponent. The purpose of group exercise, however, is to improve fitness levels. A large percentage of the population suffers from some type of back pain or injury. It is important that any movement incorporated into class includes back support with modifications for those whose abdominals and/or erector spinaes are not strong enough to maintain a supported spine. There should be no movements with the spine in flexion. Also, pay special attention to hip, knee, and toe alignment. In addition, the shoulder, elbow, and hip joints need to be protected from unsafe movements. Even if a movement can be executed slowly in alignment, it may cause torque when the speed increases.

Question 5 addresses the skill level of the class. In the group exercise setting there are a variety of fitness levels and injury histories, and faces change from day to day. Be cognizant of these factors, and modify movements in such a way that still allows the training benefits while reducing risk of injury. Movements performed at a faster speed may compromise form and alignment, and lead to greater risk of injury than those performed at moderate speed. Remember, teaching a group fitness program does not involve competition or self-defense.

III. Movement Adaptations

See AFAA's *Basic Exercise Standards and Guidelines*, sections V.B.9. and VI.

Many of the classic boxing, kickboxing, and martial arts movements have been modified for the group exercise class in order to protect the joints as well as the back. Since participants are not fighting against each other and do not have to protect themselves, the following modifications have been made to provide a workout that resembles the powerful, disciplined sports with safety in mind for the fitness enthusiast.

- The stance can be modified to make it easier to transition into traditional aerobic moves.
- The joints should be protected from torque. The knee joint is of utmost concern. Knee torque is a twisting movement that occurs when the leg rotates while the foot is weight-bearing, flat on the floor. When torque occurs, the foot is planted on the floor, the toe pointed in one direction, while the knee and hip are trying to rotate either inward or outward. This causes undue stress on the knee and ankle joints. To avoid knee torque during a pivot, lift the heel and let the ball of the foot rotate with the rest of the leg. This movement is best performed on a smooth surface that allows the foot to turn easily. It can be difficult on carpet, steps, and surfaces

with more friction, such as certain types of flooring made to reduce risk of slipping. In this case, the weight-bearing foot should be "unloaded" (with a small hop) in order to maintain hip-knee-toe alignment.

- Focus on muscle balance during the workout; punches and kicks should be performed equally on both sides.
- Participants should be shown how to modify difficult movements.
- Alignment, not kick height, should be a priority.
- The instructor should be able to identify and correct alignment problems.
- Never snap the joints to execute a punch or kick.

IV. Medical Clearance

See AFAA's *Basic Exercise Standards and Guidelines*, section V.A.5.

According to the American College of Sports Medicine (ACSM), individuals with the following conditions should receive medical clearance from a physician prior to participation.

- Anyone with a pre-existing medical condition
- Anyone with two or more risk factors*
- Anyone with diagnosed cardiovascular, pulmonary, or metabolic disease
- Anyone with signs and/or symptoms suggestive of possible cardiovascular, pulmonary, or metabolic disease (e.g., chest pain, known heart murmur, intermittent claudication, dizziness, shortness of breath, ankle edema)

*Atherosclerotic Cardiovascular Disease Risk Factors (CVD):
- Men 45 years of age or older and women 55 years of age or older
- Diagnosed high blood pressure greater than or equal to 140/90 mmHg or on blood pressure medication
- Total cholesterol levels greater than or equal to 200 mg/dL, or HDL < 35 mg/dL, or on cholesterol-lowering medication
- Cigarette smoking
- Prediabetes with a fasting blood glucose of ≥ 100 mg/dL
- Family history of heart disease or sudden death in father or male siblings prior to 55 years of age, or before 65 years of age in mother or female siblings
- Sedentary lifestyle/physical inactivity
- Obesity: BMI ≥ 30 Kg/m² or waist girth of > 100 cm

It is advisable to screen participants before they begin any type of exercise program to identify existing CVD risk factors and determine fitness levels. Sometimes this screening is conducted as part of a fitness facility's protocol before enlisting new members.

A. Cardiorespiratory Fitness Assessment

1. **Purpose**
   To determine each participant's aerobic fitness level. (NOTE: Ensure medical clearance prior to administering cardiorespiratory fitness assessment when appropriate.)

2. **Test**
   3-Minute Step Test
   Participants step on a 12-inch platform for 3 minutes at a cadence of 96 beats per minute (bpm). Arms remain at the participants' sides. At the end of the 3 minutes, participants should sit down immediately and locate their pulse. The pulse should be counted for 1 full minute to determine recovery heart rate.

3. **Results**
   The recovery heart rate will provide information about the fitness level of the participant. The quicker the heart recovers from vigorous exercise, the lower recovery heart rate will be and the greater the indication of a stronger cardiovascular system.

B. Flexibility Screening

1. **Purpose**
   An adequate range of motion is needed to execute kickboxing movements. Individuals who lack sufficient flexibility should be advised of appropriate stretching exercises to enhance range of motion. Until that time, movements should be modified accordingly or participation should be limited.

   Follow the instructions below for an assessment of range of motion at several joints. Be sure to test right and left sides of the body, as flexibility is joint-specific. In addition, have the participants warm up for at least 5 minutes prior to the tests and stretch to the point of tension. Proper spinal alignment should be maintained.

2. **Hip Flexors**
   The hip flexors (iliopsoas) consist of the iliacus and the psoas muscles, which originate at the iliac crest of the hip and spine, respectively, and insert into the femur of the thigh. Tight hip flexors will pull the pelvis anteriorly and create an increased curvature of the lumbar spine. Those with tight hip flexors are prone to increased lordosis (swayback) and related back pain.

Test: Lie on the floor in a supine position. Flex one knee and hol
the leg to the chest while the other leg is extended and resting o
the floor.

Results: Adequate hip flexor flexibility is exhibited if the calf of th
resting leg remains on the floor.

3. **Quadriceps**

The quadriceps cross the hip and knee joints. Individuals with tigh
quadriceps may be inclined to hyperextend and lock the knees.

Test: Lie on the floor in a prone position with the legs extendec
Flex one knee and bring the foot toward the buttocks. Participan
may use his/her hand to pull gently.

Results: Adequate flexibility of the quadriceps is exhibited if partic
ipant can comfortably bring the heel of one foot to the buttocks.

4. **Hamstrings**

The hamstrings group crosses the hip and knee joints. Tigh
hamstrings will pull the pelvis posteriorly, creating a flat back an
increased risk of low-back injury.

Test: Lie on the floor in a supine position with legs extended an
resting on the floor. Raise one leg to form a 90° angle with th
torso.

Results: Do not use the arms to hold the leg in place. Adequat
flexibility of the hamstrings group is exhibited if participant ca
achieve this position without bending the knee while keeping th
calf of the resting leg on the floor.

VI. Hydration

Participants should be advised to hydrate before, during, and after exercise
when appropriate based on individual needs, in order to replenish neces
sary body fluids and to maintain electrolyte balance. Generally, partici
pants should drink approximately 8–12 ounces of fluid shortly befor
exercise. (Refer to AFAA's *Basic Exercise Standards and Guidelines.*)

VII. Pre-Class Instruction

The instructor should introduce himself or herself to the class, announc
the type of class it is, and ask if there are any participants new to kick
boxing. Also ask if anyone has any special conditions, such as pregnancy o
an injury. Always remember to stress the importance of working at a
individual pace and modifying movements to suit personal needs an
goals. Water breaks should be given to the class or a general announcemen
should be made to encourage the drinking of water several time
throughout the workout.

VIII. Warm-Up

As with any vigorous exercise session, it is important to warm up the body. The warm-up can enhance performance and reduce the risk of injury. Physiologically, the warm-up provides time for blood to be redirected from the organs to the working muscles, for the heart to adapt to increased demands, for the joints to become lubricated, for the muscles to become more pliable, and for the respiratory system to increase ventilation. The warm-up also acts as a rehearsal for the mode of exercise to follow.

AFAA's *Basic Exercise Standards and Guidelines*, section VIII.B., recommends a combination of movement rehearsal, limbering, and optional light preparatory stretches. The limbering movements should be full range of motion, without resistance, and progress from smaller to bigger as the warm-up progresses. The movements should include stretches for every part of the body, to prepare for the full-body workout to follow, and mimic some of the movements involved in the kickboxing routine. The preparatory stretches should be held for less than 15 seconds (8–16 beats of music), and involve all major muscle groups heavily involved in the workout (the recommendation to do some shorter joint-specific stretches for kickboxing is warranted due to the ballistic nature of the movements). The muscles to be stretched should include all of the following: (a) triceps, (b) upper back, (c) pectoralis major, (d) latissimus dorsi, (e) internal/external obliques, (f) hip adductors, (g) quadriceps group, (h) hip flexors, (i) hamstring group, and (j) calves. The low back should be properly prepared (in accordance with AFAA's *Basic Exercise Standards and Guidelines*, section VIII.B.3.), as heavy demands are placed on the back as a stabilizer during most of the kicks and punches. High-intensity movements, such as the boxer's shuffle, jumping jacks, or jump rope, as well as strength training movements (e.g., push-ups), should be avoided until the entire body has had sufficient time to warm up.

Those participants who do not exhibit adequate spinal flexibility and strength, as well as adequate flexibility throughout the body, should modify the workout to avoid undue stress on the joints and connective tissue, or they should abstain from participation until such time as flexibility is adequate to perform the movements safely.

The warm-up should include a review of the basic punch and kick forms at a slower speed than they will be executed during the workout. This will prepare the muscles and joints, allow the opportunity to reinforce proper form and alignment, and teach new participants the basic movements.

IX. Class Formats

There are several different ways to format a kickboxing class. Choose to use one or all of the following formats during a given class. Regardless of the chosen format, when combining traditional aerobic dance movements, such as jogs, toe taps, step touches, and jumping jacks with kicks an punches, be sure to adhere to these safety guidelines.

- Whether the mechanical stress is high- or low-impact, the he should come in contact with the floor with each step.
- Avoid lateral high-impact movements, such as jumping jacks c high-impact grapevines, for the first 3 minutes of the cardio se tion to allow the ankles to warm up.
- Avoid peak or extreme high-intensity movements for the first minutes of the cardio section.
- Don't jog on toes, as this shortens the calf muscles and Achille tendon.
- Don't lean forward, as this can contribute to shin splints and kne stress.
- Do keep the body balanced over the entire foot and not backwar on the heels.
- Don't kick heel up to the buttocks, as this arches the lower bacl Keep knees aligned with toes.
- Choose movements that are appropriate for the fitness level of th class.
- Do not jump on one leg more than eight times in succession be cause of the risk of injury caused by repeated impact. (See AFAA *Basic Exercise Standards and Guidelines*, section VIII.C.3.)

A. Combination/Choreographed

This style of teaching is characterized by movements that are se quenced in patterns that are built around the phrase of the music an can be repeated and recycled. Common aerobic dance movement such as grapevines, step touches, mambos, and jacks, are used alon with punches and kicks to create combinations. For example, a jab c cross can be added to the end of a grapevine.

B. Drill Style

Similar to calisthenic or military-style cardiorespiratory classes, dri style is characterized by many repetitions of the same movement se quence. Movements may or may not be in time with the music de pending on the instructor's individual preference. Music is usuall used to keep cadence, but movements are not usually on the phras of the music.

C. Freestyle

This style can vary from instructor to instructor. Partner drills, group formations, and circuit stations are examples of what might be seen in this type of class. Music is often used for background.

D. Step Kickboxing

This type of class utilizes the step and step choreography combined with kickboxing punches and kicks. The movements may be woven into step choreography or used in floor-mix patterns built into the step choreography. For example, a front kick can be added at the end of a turn step, and an L-step can end with a side kick instead of a tap. Also, try shifting back and forth from step choreography to floor patterns that include kickboxing movements. Be sure to adhere to the safety guidelines for step, which include the following.

1. Music should be 118–128 bpm or up to 135 bpm for those participants skilled enough to maintain proper alignment.
2. Do not step forward off the step.
3. Do not step with back to the step.
4. Do not jump off the step.
5. Limit single-lead steps to 1 minute in duration.
6. Limit lunges and propulsion to one minute in duration.
7. Step to the center of the step with the full foot.
8. Step lightly (do not pound the foot).
9. Step up with a full body, lean from the ankle; do not bend at the hip or waist.
10. Extend fully at the hip and knee joints.
11. Step down close to the step bringing the full foot to the floor without bouncing.
12. Be sure knees do not flex beyond 90° when weight bearing.
13. Watch the step periodically.
14. Do not lower the heel to the floor when performing lunges and repeaters.

E. Intensity

See AFAA's *Basic Exercise Standards and Guidelines*, section VIII.C.2.

A class may be designed as steady state, variable intensity (intermittent training), or interval in nature. A steady-state class would look like a flat-top bell curve if the intensity level was plotted. This is similar to most traditional aerobic dance classes. A variable-intensity class would bring the participants into their target heart rate zones and then vary intensity throughout the workout, maintaining target heart rates. A[n] interval class would consist of work loads high enough to begin relyin[g] more heavily on the lactic acid system or phosphagen system (depen[d] ing on intensity and duration) followed by periods of active recovery [a] drop in intensity utilizing primarily the aerobic energy system).

X. Music

Instructors should have a basic understanding of the beat and phrase of th[e] music. The use of music in the class will vary with the instructor's ind[i]vidual style. Music speed should be slow enough to allow proper executio[n] of skills through a full range of motion. The recommended range [is] 125–135 bpm (slower for step kickboxing; see section IX.D.1.), with [a] maximum speed of 140 bpm for participants skilled enough to maintai[n] proper alignment.

XI. Interval Training

Class format determines if the workout will be steady state or interv[al] training. When talking about interval training, many envision a worko[ut] that alternates back and forth between different modes of exercise. Tr[ue] interval training is characterized by periods of intense work followed b[y] periods of lower-intensity active recovery. One of the benefits of interv[al] training is the greater cardiorespiratory training stimulus it produc[es] compared to that in steady state training.

Additional benefits include higher-intensity exercise in a given tim[e,] resulting in more calories burned. The interval training stimulus may max[i]mize the improvement in VO_{2max}, as well as result in significant improv[e]ments in mitochondrial density. Note that the higher the intensity of th[e] work portion of the interval, the longer the recovery period should be.

In addition to these aerobic training benefits, high-intensity trainin[g] stresses the glycolytic system in muscles and results in significant lacta[te] accumulation. Repeated exposure to elevated levels of lactate will impro[ve] the body's tolerance of high-intensity exercise, as the rate of lactate remov[al] is directly related to lactate concentration (the greater the concentratio[n,] the greater the removal). Interval training that increases blood lactate leve[ls] will stimulate improvement in its removal.

XII. Cross Training

Cross training is the use of several types of activities to develop one fitne[ss] component. This practice can help prevent boredom, and help prepare f[or] a wider range of activities and physical challenges. It can also reduce th[e] risk of overuse injury and overtraining because the same muscles, bone[s] and joints are not continuously subjected to the stresses of the sam[e] activity.

Kickboxing can be used along with traditional aerobics, step training, group cycling, treadmills, stair steppers, and rowing machines for a diversified, well-balanced cardiorespiratory endurance training program. For those who have spent the last few years step training several times a week, kickboxing would be a good cross training choice. While step training is predominately leg work, a kickboxing class incorporates balanced work for both the upper and lower body.

XIII. Isolation Training

Isolation training usually refers to resistance training that targets individual muscles or muscle groups. In many kickboxing classes, push-ups and abdominal work are performed at the end. The push-up will strengthen the pectoralis major, anterior deltoids, and the triceps—muscles that are active in many of the punches performed in class. While this may help the force at which participants will be able to punch, other muscles should also be trained in the interest of muscle-balancing.

Abdominal strengthening is appropriate, as stronger abs are better able to maintain proper alignment throughout a kickboxing workout as well as throughout the day. This is an extremely important part of maintaining a healthy back. The opposing muscles to the abdominals, the erector spinae, should also be targeted in the isolation section of the class in order to achieve balance between agonist and antagonist.

A good way to practice movements and build muscular endurance is to perform the basic punches and kicks at half-time. The practice will also improve balance and teach proper execution.

A. Push-Ups

Key points for proper execution of a push-up include the following.

1. Position hands on the floor shoulder-width apart or slightly wider.
2. Point fingers straight ahead.
3. Soften elbows; don't lock them.
4. Contract abdominals.
5. Raise the buttocks slightly when the legs are fully extended.
6. Distribute body weight evenly, regardless of position.
7. Descend and ascend smoothly, and do not let the body sag in the middle. Lead with the chest, not the abdominals.

Vary the intensity of a push-up by changing the speed, range of motion and body position.

Standing Push-up Against a Wall—Limited training benefit as they do not work against gravity. Recommended for individuals with rotator cuff problems and/or limited strength, and pregnant women.

All-Fours Push-up—Knees on the floor directly under hips. Forehead lowers toward the floor. Less intense than full and modified push-up.

Modified Push-up—Same as all-fours except knees are behind the hips. Keep the knees hip-width apart for balance.

Full-Body—Toes instead of knees are on the floor with buttocks slightly lifted.

Incline/Decline Push-up—The incline push-up elevates the upper body (hands on a step). This will decrease the intensity a bit from the standard full-body push-up and change the angle of work. The decline push-up elevates the feet (feet up on a step) and increases intensity from the full-body push-up while also changing the angle of work.

B. Abdominal Work

Key points for proper execution of abdominal strengthening include the following.

1. Lie on the floor in a supine position.
2. Bend the knees and keep the feet flat on the floor.
3. Position the pelvis to help the lower back and torso maintain neutral spine. The lower back remains on the floor or as close to the floor as possible without creating an extreme posterior tilt.
4. Bring the head, neck, and shoulders up off the floor, allowing the scapula to clear the floor at the top of the tilt.
5. Flex the spine approximately 30–45°.
6. When rotating the spine, keep the lower body stationary, lead with the shoulder—not the elbow—and do not roll the hips from side to side.
7. When elevating both legs off the floor, keep the knees above the hips (thighs perpendicular to the floor) to protect the back. Do not use a swinging motion.
8. Exhale while contracting the abdominals.
9. The arms, hands, or finger tips may support the head, but avoid interlacing the fingers behind the head and pulling the neck.
10. Change arm position, speed, and range of motion for variety.

C. Erector Spinae

Key points for proper execution of erector spinae (lower back) exercises include the following.

1. Lie prone with both legs extended.
2. Keep pelvis in neutral alignment with abdominals contracted.

3. Lift one leg at a time.

4. Do not place hands under hips.

5. Keep chest and rib cage in contact with the floor.

6. Variations include (a) modified cobra (on forearms held for 20 seconds), (b) lifting one straight leg at a time to hip height, (c) alternating straight leg lifts, (d) lifting one leg and the opposite arm, or (e) lifting both arms with torso slightly raised while legs remain on the floor.

7. Intensity modifications include (a) extending one or both arms overhead, (b) bringing arms close to the torso at sides, or (c) bending elbows with forearms under the head.

8. Movement should be slow to moderate.

9. Movements should be controlled and without momentum.

XIV. Cool-Down

End of class cool-down should consist of full-range static stretches that are held a minimum of 15 seconds or for 1 to 4 repetitions of 15–30 seconds up to 60 seconds. All major muscles groups should be targeted, especially those used heavily during the workout. Benefits of a proper cool-down include relaxation, improved range of motion, and removal of metabolic waste. Hold stretches in proper alignment without bouncing to avoid injury and invoking the stretch reflex. Muscles that should be stretched after class include the following.

- Hip adductors
- Upper back (trapezius and rhomboids)
- Hip abductors
- Pectoralis major
- Hamstring group
- Deltoids
- Quadriceps group
- Internal and external obliques
- Hip flexors
- Triceps
- Latissimus dorsi

11

STANDARDS and GUIDELINES for
for Step Training

I. Introduction

Since its origin in the late 1980s, step training has continued to be popular form of high-intensity, low-impact cardiorespiratory exercise, an has advanced to new and exciting levels. Although relatively new to th group exercise class, the step has been used for decades in athletic trainin; physical therapy, and as a tool for submaximal testing to assess cardiore spiratory fitness. As instructors continue to develop step classes that ar interesting and challenging for their participants, they must be aware o and incorporate, the current safety guidelines in conjunction with AFAA *Basic Exercise Standards and Guidelines.*

II. Step Training Recommendations

Detailed discussions on step training research, choreography, injur prevention, and teaching techniques are found in AFAA's *Step Training: Manual for Instructors.* As is true with any form of cardiorespirator training, programming recommendations for step training should be care fully considered. When beginning a step program, exercisers should b advised to begin with a moderate program and to gradually progress th program as they become accustomed to this type of exercise. Table 11.1 outlines step training recommendations.

Table 11.1. Level	Recommended Step Height	Suggested Stepping Duration
Level 1		
Someone who has not participated in a regular exercise program	4 inches	10–20 minutes
Level 2		
A regular exerciser who is new to step training	4 to 6 inches	10–20 minutes
Level 3		
A regular stepper	4 to 8 inches	minimum of 20–30 minutes, no more than 60 minute:
Level 4		
A highly skilled and regular stepper	4 to 10 inches	20–60 minutes

III. Class Format

A. Pre-Class Instructions

Duration: 2–3 minutes

Purpose: To familiarize participants with step training technique and guidelines

B. Warm-Up

Tempo: 120–134 bpm

Duration: 8–12 minutes

Purpose: To increase core temperature as well as prepare the muscles and joints for movements that will follow. This can be accomplished by combining movement rehearsal, limbering, as well as optional light preparatory stretches. A proper warm-up should prepare the body for vigorous exercise, and may reduce the risk of injury. (See AFAA's *Basic Exercise Standards and Guidelines*, section VIII.B.)

C. Cardiorespiratory Training

Tempo: 118–128 bpm*

Duration: 20–60 minutes

Purpose: To improve the heart, circulatory, and pulmonary systems. This can be accomplished by utilizing a variety of training methods that target cardiorespiratory endurance. (See AFAA's *Basic Exercise Standards and Guidelines*, section VIII.C.)

*128–135 bpm may be appropriate for highly-skilled steppers as long as proper alignment and technique are maintained.

D. Muscular Strength and Endurance Training

Tempo: 120–130 bpm

Duration: 15–20 minutes

Purpose: Important component to overall health. Benefits include an improved ability to perform everyday activities, increased muscle mass, increased metabolism, stronger bones, decreased risk of injury, improved posture and symmetry, and improved athletic performance.

E. Flexibility and Final Class

Tempo: up to 100 bpm

Duration: 5–10 minutes*

* (or time to complete a minimum of 1 set for each muscle group)

Purpose: Flexibility training improves joint mobility and increases range of motion in order to decrease the risk of potential injury and enhance physical performance. The final class segment is designed to promote mind-body awareness and facilitate the relaxation response, a state in which the heart rate and blood pressure are decreased, muscles are relaxed, and physiological stress is reduced. It is an optimal time for participant education. It also provides a sense of completion.

IV. Body Alignment and Stepping Technique

To minimize the risk of injury and maximize the conditioning benefits of stepping, teach the following body alignment and stepping technique guidelines to step class participants. Continually monitor participants' form, and coach as necessary.

A. Body Alignment
- Shoulders back and relaxed
- Chest lifted and body erect
- Abdominals contracted to support torso
- Neutral spine
- Knees relaxed, not locked
- Avoid hyperextension of joints
- Avoid twisting or torquing of joints

B. Stepping Technique
- Use a full body lean. Do not bend at the waist or hips.
- Knee flexion should not exceed 90° when weight bearing.
- Watch the platform periodically.
- Focus on the feet first. Add arm movements when proficient with the footwork.
- Step to the center of the step. Do not let feet hang off the edge.
- Stay close to the platform when stepping down.
- Don't step down with back to the platform.
- Step lightly. Avoid pounding feet on the step.
- Allow whole foot to contact the floor and step (except during propulsion movements).
- When setting up or breaking down, use proper lifting technique and carry the step close to the body.

V. Variables that Affect Intensity

As in any form of cardiorespiratory activity, the exercise session should begin with a moderate intensity and increase gradually. The participant should remain within the training range for the designated period of time and decrease gradually to the pre-exercise level. Creating the bell-shaped intensity curve will allow the participant to adapt both physiologically and biomechanically to the exercise. The instructor should inform the participants of methods to adapt intensity to an appropriate level.

A number of variables were found to affect exercise intensity during step training. The most significant increases occurred with the following two variables.

- Step height
- Choreography

A. Step Height as a Variable to Modify Exercise Intensity

Intensity and step height appear to be linear in relationship. Thus, an increase in step height will produce an increased energy cost. Participants are encouraged to select a step height that will allow an appropriate training stimulus without compromising form and technique.

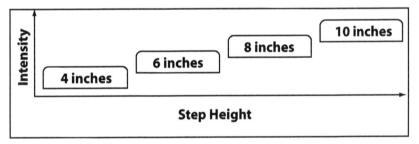

B. Choreography as a Variable to Modify Exercise Intensity

Movement patterns may be designed to manipulate the intensity of a step class. Factors, such as lever length, elevation of levers, range of motion, speed of movement (e.g., propulsions, power movements), and traveling, will dictate the intensity of the step skill or combination of skills. Smaller movements, such as the basic step and V-step, are generally low-intensity movements that may be used in the building and decreasing phases of the bell curve design. Movements, such as lunges and traveling knee lifts, are higher in intensity and should be interspersed throughout the workout (rather than placed all together) to avoid overworking the class participants. A summary of step movement skills and the measure of intensity for each is provided in Table 11.2.

Table 11.2.

Step Movement	VO$_2$ (ml/kg/min)	METs
Basic Step	26.2	7.5
Across-the-top	26.6	7.6
Alternating Knee-lift	28.7	8.2
Repeater Knee-lift	32.0	9.1
Alternating Lunge	32.7	9.3
Turn-step with Lunge	35.0	10.1

C. Effect of Power vs. Traditional Step Training

When step skills are performed quickly, the intensity of the movement is increased. Propulsion movements and power skills demonstrate a higher intensity than when they are performed in a traditional step training manner. A summary of traditional and power step movement patterns and the measure of intensity for each is provided in Table 11.3.

Table 11.3.

Step Height	Heart Rates		VO$_2$ (ml/kg/min)		METs	
	Traditional	Power	Traditional	Power	Traditional	Power
4 inches	138 bpm	158 bpm	26.5	34.5	7.6	9.9
6 inches	144 bpm	163 bpm	29.0	37.0	8.3	10.6
8 inches	155 bpm	170 bpm	32.4	38.7	9.3	11.1

As mentioned earlier, choreographic variables, such as lever length, range of motion, elevation, traveling, arm movements, and the inclusion of power movements, will affect intensity. Select movements that are appropriate for the skill and fitness level of the particular class.

D. The Effect of Music Tempo on Exercise Intensity

Although increases in step tempo provide an additional energy cost during exercise, the increase is minimal when compared to other variables examined. Be aware that safety may be compromised at faster tempos, as proper form and technique are more difficult to achieve. Evaluate the risk/benefit ratio of increased music tempo and select a music tempo that allows class participants to execute the movements in proper form.

Guidelines currently recommend a stepping cadence of 118–128 bpm to provide sufficient physiological stimulus and allow participants to maintain proper form and body alignment. This guideline is appropriate for the general population in the group exercise setting. The skilled and highly-conditioned stepper may be able to maintain form and technique at slightly faster tempos—up to 135 bpm. Continually monitor the class. Be aware of participants' form, and adjust tempo accordingly.

As with any mode of exercise, injury potential in step training is a significant consideration. Minimal research has been performed thus far to examine the immediate and long-term biomechanical effects of step training. Information available to date, however, suggests that step training is a safe mode of cardiorespiratory exercise.

VI. Biomechanical Considerations

A. Biomechanical Effects on the Feet

Francis et al., of San Diego University (1994), examined the biomechanical forces applied during step training. With the use of a sensitive scale known as a force plate, the initial study compared vertical impact, friction forces, and time to peak force during three different modes of training: (a) walking, (b) running, and (c) step training. The work of Francis suggests that the biomechanical forces of step training are similar to those of walking.

As the first foot down off of the step receives the greatest impact force, a single lead leg should not be maintained for longer than a 1-minute duration. As the novice stepper may experience muscular fatigue quickly, it may be necessary to change the lead leg more frequently when working with this population. As lunges and propulsion movements exhibit greater impact forces and are high-intensity movements, they should be limited in duration (i.e., approximately 1 minute) and interspersed throughout the workout. Movements of this nature should be reserved for individuals with higher skill and fitness levels.

Biomechanical forces discussed in this study were collected at a stepping rate of 120 bpm. As the protective mechanisms within the foot engage at approximately 1/20th of a second after forces are applied, step tempo is a significant consideration. A moderately-paced movement will allow the protective mechanisms to engage before peak forces are applied. In contrast, a faster stepping rate will increase the force and decrease the protective mechanism efficiency. Additionally, a moderately-paced movement will allow the entire foot to be placed on the floor and provide a greater surface area to absorb the impact forces.

There is one exception—only the ball of the foot should be placed on the floor during lunging movements to avoid placing a rapid stretch on the Achilles tendon.

B. Biomechanical Effects on the Knees

The knee is a structurally complicated hinge joint. The stability of the knee depends primarily on the integrity of the supporting ligaments and musculature. The knee becomes particularly vulnerable as the degree of weight-bearing knee flexion increases. Flexion beyond 90° provides excessive force (as much as 8 times the body weight) to the knee, creating an unnecessary risk of injury. Range of motion at the knee should be limited, therefore, to no more than a 90° angle when weight bearing.

When the knee is supporting the body weight, the foot becomes locked to the floor. Pivoting at this point causes twisting of the support leg and undue stress to the knee. Pivoting movements should only be performed when the leg is non-weight bearing or "unloaded."

Participants with prior knee pain or injury should obtain a physician's approval, and should stop step training immediately if pain or discomfort is experienced.

VII. Summary

Step training continues to be a form of cardiorespiratory training that is enjoyed by group exercise participants. Instructors have a responsibility to lead participants through a workout that is both physiologically and biomechanically sound. The guidelines provided here and in AFAA's *Step Training: A Manual for Instructors* reflect current industry guidelines that are based on scientific research performed to date.

12 STANDARDS and GUIDELINES for for Mat Science®

I. Introduction

Mat Science brings to the group fitness instructor a unique integration of a variety of movements derived from the classic disciplines and philosophies of dance, Pilates, and yoga along with basic conditioning exercises to reflect the latest fusion trends within the industry. It is based on a progressive exercise series that can accommodate most, if not all, fitness levels to improve strength and endurance, joint mobility, flexibility, balance, and coordination while focusing on breathing and mindful movements. This information is to be used in conjunction with AFAA's *Basic Exercise Standards and Guidelines.*

II. Philosophy

* Mat Science takes group floor-based fitness classes one step beyond current exercise practices by reintroducing mindfulness, attention to form, exercise execution, and the breath back into the classroom as part of every workout.
* Mat Science encompasses the Eastern philosophy of yoga, the holistic approach of centering and conditioning from Pilates, as well as the application of current exercise science and biomechanics. As a result, classes are safe, effective, and mind/body oriented, leading to more meaningful exercise practices.
* The philosophy of Mat Science is to embrace the original disciplines on which almost every floor exercise used in group fitness today is based and meld classic training with contemporary exercise.

III. Styles

* A typical Mat Science class is a blend of yoga postures, Pilates exercises, as well as exercises from a more contemporary fitness floor class or dance (e.g., floor/barre). Class varies in length from 30 to 90 minutes.
* The exercise selection is dependent on the instructor's level of knowledge in the various disciplines on which Mat Science is based (e.g., a class may be more yoga-based than dance therapy-based or vice versa).
* A Mat Science class follows similar safety guidelines recommended for all group exercise class formats: (a) begin with a warm-up, (b) increase intensity gradually by selecting appropriate exercises to increase body heat for strength and deeper flexibility movements, and (c) finish with a cool-down.

IV. Benefits of Mat Science

- Improve muscle tone and shape.
- Improve strength, endurance, joint mobility, flexibility, and extensibility of connective tissue.
- Improve muscle balance, alignment, coordination, and kinesthetic awareness.
- Improve breathing.
- Improve posture and alignment, which may relieve back strain and other postural-related disorders, and improve general mobility to allow more fluidly and gracefulness in movement.
- Improve emotional balance and mental clarity.
- Stimulate circulation and blood oxygenation, as well as boost immune system.

V. Exercise Principles

A. Principle of Balance

Balance is achieved when all of the body's muscles work synergistically without exerted or strained effort, breathing is tempered and even, and the mind is clear and free of extraneous thought. During a Mat Science class, "balance" is when the body, mind, and breath are connected in movement.

Balance involves:
- symmetrical balance;
- balance between strength and flexibility; and
- balance between aggressive/passive approach to the exercise.

Imbalance occurs due to:
- improper focus; and
- weak stabilizer muscles.

B. Principle of Extension

Extension refers to:
- muscle elongation out and away from the joint, creating freedom of unrestricted joint mobility;
- "activating" one's muscles; and
- working in opposition and angle of pull of a muscle to a joint

C. Principle of Alignment

See AFAA's *Basic Exercise Standards and Guidelines*, section VI.C.

1. Positioning in proper alignment before moving can make the difference in proper execution.
2. Always maintain a neutral relationship between spine, pelvis, and extremities.

D. Principle of Range of Motion

1. Every exercise has a minimum and maximum boundary or limitation, which determines personal range of motion.
2. Use the breath to assist deepening into a stretch or position.

E. Principle of Progression

Progression refers to:

- exercise selection; and
- a series of exercises that can be performed in a specific order in relation to each other because they have a similar goal.

Use the principle of range of motion to determine a starting point in each position.

F. Principle of Flow

1. Transition smoothly from one posture to the next, using the breath to assist the process.
2. Sequentially, movements that are held and those that move with the breath may be combined.

G. Principle of Breath

1. The principle of breath acknowledges the breath as an integral part of every movement.
2. Choose the breath pattern that best complements the movement.

VI. Class Format Guidelines

Though the body of a class will vary depending on length of class, participant levels, and instructor exercise selection, AFAA recommends the following.

- Always begin a Mat Science class with an initial warm-up and breathing.
- Include a progressive series of exercises that build heat; increase both strength and flexibility in the body of the workout.
- Always finish a Mat Science class with a final cool-down period to relax and restore.
- If teaching more than one Mat Science class during the week, vary activities, progression, and intensity levels at each session.
- Select different objectives or purposes for class formats (e.g., "Today, we'll concentrate a little more on back strengthening," or "Today, let's explore minimal and maximal boundaries during our forward bends").
- Move fluidly and mindfully with each exercise; speed is not an option.
- Use the principles of Mat Science to fine-tune movements.

- Develop appropriate levels of intensity of progressions for each movement used.
- Modify movements for participants who need special attention.

VII. Warm-Up

A. Time
10 to 15 minutes

B. Purpose
This initial warm-up is to introduce the breath so that body, mind, and breath can be linked for the entire workout. These movements should not be too challenging, but bring participants into mindfulness of their own bodies and how they're moving.

C. Include
1. The warm-up should include some form of breathing activity—alone or with a movement.
   Examples: Supine Breathing, Half Sun Breaths, Moving Twist with a Sun Breath
2. Movements should include limbering and fluid motion as preparation for more challenging exercises to come.
   Examples: Potted Palm Series, Cat, Cat with Downward Facing Dog in Vinyasa (flow)

D. Positions to Avoid
During the warm-up, avoid positions that require more range of motion and deep openings of the joints (e.g., hips, shoulders, and spine). Save these activities for when the body is more prepared (i.e., at least 10 minutes into workout, depending on how much heat has been produced and how much preparation has been done in the initial warm-up).
   Examples: Boundangular, Sitting Angular, Straight Leg Forward Bend, Back Bending

VIII. Body of Workout (Based on Class Goals)

The following types of activities are recommended as part of a complete Mat Science class. Depending on the focus of the class that day (e.g., strength, alignment, back bending, etc.), there may be more of one category of movements included in the format. For a well-rounded class, include activities from each category.

A. Time
About 40 minutes total for this entire section (time will vary for each type of activity listed)

B. Heat-Building Movements

1. Purpose: To increase core temperature and muscle core temperature

2. Mild heat builders can be utilized as part of the warm-up; more dynamic heat builders are best introduced following initial warm-up.
   Examples (mild heat builders): Cat, Bridge/Moving Bridge, Bali Seal, Moving Low Lunge
   Examples (dynamic heat builders): Cat to Downward Facing Dog, Hundred, Roll-ups

3. Dynamic heat builders can also combine two or more movements together in a flow series to increase heat.
   Examples: Plank to Chatarunga to Downward Facing Dog to Cobra, Push-up to Plank Pose (three to six times)

4. Some heat-building exercises also increase strength at the same time; include these last as a transition into strength.
   Examples: Plank Pose with variations (with alternate leg raises, with a push-up)

5. Avoid sacrificing form and stabilization for movement.

C. Strength-Building Movements

1. Purpose: To increase dynamic and functional strength of upper core and lower extremities as both primary movers and stabilizers

2. Include these moves at least 20 minutes into class when the body is fully warm and prepared.

3. Use transition moves, counter-moves (i.e., move of opposition to balance muscles worked), or resting poses between series of poses as necessary to relax, refocus, or realign.
   Examples: Child's Pose after Plank series, Bridge after an abdominal strengthening series, Forward Bend after back bending series

4. Upper body strengtheners
   Examples: Push-ups, Chatarungas (slow and completed with hover), Swimming, Downward Facing Dog (held with the breath), Planks and Side Planks

5. Torso strengtheners
   Examples: Scale, Single Leg Stretch, Crisscross, Planks, Back Bends, Knee Drops

6. Lower body strengtheners
   Examples: Low Lunge, Leg Circles (performed slowly with active legs), Kneeling Side Kicks, Side-lying Side Kicks

D. Back Bends

1. Purpose: To energize the body and increase range of motion, flexibility, and strength of the spine, as well as open up the front of the body

2. Back bends should be included later in class, when the body is thoroughly warm and prepared; if the body has cooled down, rebuild heat first or begin with a moving back bend series before holding in any position.

3. These exercises should be performed progressively and slowly. Back bending can be mild (e.g., Low Lunge) or more challenging (e.g., Locust).
   Examples: Progression—opposite arm and leg to Sphinx to Cobra

4. Back bending can be static, increasing range of motion gently

5. Back bending can be performed as a flow series with breath
   Examples: Cobra: inhale in four counts and lift; exhale and lower in four counts, then repeat three to six times; Moving Locust

6. Back bending can be performed in a flow series with a forward bend
   Examples: In Low Lunge—bring arms forward, bring chest to knee, return to Low Lunge, arms extended above head

7. Balance back bending with a counter move of forward bending (active or restorative) for release
   Examples: Staff Pose Forward Bend (active), Child's Pose (restorative)

E. Forward Bends

1. Purpose: To lengthen back muscles, increase hamstrings flexibility, and for relaxation and calming of the mind through the use of the breath

2. Create heat in the body before performing forward bends.

3. Avoid being overly aggressive; ease into forward bends slowly. Choose progressive exercises for both back and hamstrings.
   Examples: Potted Palm Forward Bend to Staff Pose Forward Bend or to Sitting Angular Forward Bend

4. Balance forward bends with back bends.

F. Twisting

1. Purpose: Torso rotation (twisting motions) improves spine range of motion and back flexibility, and allows the breath to reach deeper into the abdomen and into the thoracic and lower spine (out of the chest and shoulders).

2. Twisting can be static or performed with flow and the breath.
   Examples: In Potted Palm Twist, then with Sun Breaths

3. Twisting for Mat Science is performed sitting or lying supine, and can also be used as a cool-down or restorative movement.
   Examples: Bent Knee Twist, Long Lying Stretch
4. For balance, always twist equally in both directions as part of the movement sequence

G. Joint Openers

1. Purpose: To increase joint range of motion (particularly shoulders and hips) and increase flexibility of muscles that have the tendency to be tight (hamstrings). These stretches are considered "deep" openers.
   Examples: Bull Seat Prep, 1/2 Staff Pose Twist, Sitting Angular Leg Extension, Long Lying Stretch
2. Include these exercises during the last half of class when the body is warm and fluid (the body uses created heat to stretch without straining).
3. Use the principle of range of motion to establish minimal and maximal boundaries. Ease into each position carefully and slowly.
4. Use the breath to move deeper into position; be cautious of any joint pain.

H. Transition (Resting) Movements

1. Purpose: To relax from exertion after a challenging series (e.g., Plank/Downward Facing Dog Vinyasa, Scale Progression) or movement (joint openers); to reconnect and focus on the breath; and to transition smoothly and easily to another movement
2. Do use these poses when a break is needed
   Examples: Child's Pose, Extended Seal, supine knees to chest

IX. Cool-Down

A. Time
5 to 10 minutes

B. Purpose
To use the breath to slow down and relax, release from any deep joint openers, twisting, or strength movements. Choose movements that are more restorative in nature.
   Examples: Bent Knee Twists, Long Lying Stretch, Side-lying Shoulder Circles

C. Avoid
- Heat building
- Moves that are too active or strenuous
- Back bend at the end of class

Part IV

References

GENERAL GROUP EXERCISE

Basic Exercise Standards and Guidelines

1. Albano, C., & Terbizan, D.J. (2001). Heart rate and RPE differences between aerobic dance and cardio-kickboxing. Abstract. *Medicine & Science in Sports & Exercise, 33*(5), S604.

2. Alter, M.J. (2004). *The science of flexibility* (3rd ed.). Champaign, IL: Human Kinetics.

3. American College of Sports Medicine. (2007). *ACSM's health/fitness facility standards and guidelines* (3rd ed.). Champaign, IL: Human Kinetics.

4. American College of Sports Medicine. (2007). ACSM's position stand on exercise and fluid replacement. *Medicine & Science in Sports & Exercise, 39*(2), 377–390.

5. American College of Sports Medicine. (2009). *ACSM's exercise management for persons with chronic diseases and disabilities* (3rd ed.). Champaign, IL: Human Kinetics.

6. American College of Sports Medicine. (2010). *ACSM's resource manual for guidelines for exercise testing and prescription* (6th ed.). Baltimore, MD: Lippincott Williams & Wilkins.

7. American College of Sports Medicine. (2010). *ACSM's guidelines for exercise testing and prescription* (8th ed.). Baltimore, MD: Lippincott Williams & Wilkins.

8. Baechle, T., & Earle, T. (2003). *Essentials of strength training and conditioning* (3rd ed.). Champaign, IL: Human Kinetics.

9. Baker, A. (1998). *Bicycling medicine: Cycling nutrition, physiology, and injury prevention and treatment for riders of all levels.* New York, NY: Fireside.

10. Bell, J., & Bassey, E. (1994). High and low-impact aerobic dance heart rate and VO2 responses. *European Journal of Applied Physiology, 68,* 20–24.

11. Bellinger, B., St. Clair, G.A., Oelofse, A., & Lambert, M. (1997). Energy expenditure of a noncontact boxing training session compared with submaximal treadmill running. *Medicine & Science in Sports & Exercise, 29*(12), 1653–1656.

12. Bernando, L.M. (2007). The effectiveness of Pilates training in healthy adults: An appraisal of the research literature. *Journal of Bodywork Movement Therapies, 11*(2), 106–110.

13. Berry, M.J., Cline, C.C., Berry, C.B., & Davis, M.A. (1992). A comparison between two forms of aerobic dance and treadmill running. *Medicine & Science in Sports & Exercise, 24*(8), 946–951.

14. Bijlani, R.L., Vempati, R.P., Yadav, R.K., Ray, R.B., Gupta, V., Sharma, R., Mehta, N., & Mahapatra, S.C. (2005). A brief but comprehensive lifestyle education program based on yoga reduces risk factors for cardiovascular disease and diabetes mellitus. *Journal of Alternative & Complementary Medicine*, 11(2), 267–274.

15. Bissonnette, D., Guzman, N., McMillan, L., Catalano, S., Giroux, M., Greenlaw, K., Vivolo, S., Otto, R.M., & Wygand, J. (1994). The energy requirements of karate aerobic exercise versus low impact aerobic dance. *Medicine & Science in Sports & Exercise*, 26(5), S58.

16. Brown, P., & O'Neill, M. (1990). A retrospective survey of the incidence and pattern of aerobics-related injuries in Victoria, 1987-1988. *Australian Journal of Science and Medicine in Sport*, 22(3), 77–81.

17. Bushman, B. (2002). Female athlete triad: Education is key. *ACSM's Certified News*, 12(2), June. Retrieved May 1, 2009, from http://www.acsm.org

18. Church, T.S., Earnest, C.P., Skinner, J.S., & Blair, S.N. (2007). Effects of different doses of physical activity on cardiorespiratory fitness among sedentary, overweight or obese postmenopausal women with elevated blood pressure: A randomized controlled trial. *Journal of American Medical Association*, May, 297, 2081–2091.

19. Clapp, J., & Little, K. (1994). The physiological response of instructors and participants to three aerobics regimens. *Medicine & Science in Sports & Exercise*, 26(8), 1041–1046.

20. Davis, M., & Bahamonde, R.E. (2000). A survey of shoes and injury characteristics of aerobic instructors. *Medicine & Science in Sports & Exercise*, 32(5), S1520.

21. DeVreede, P., Samson, M., & VanMeeteren, N. (2005). Functional-task exercise vs. resistance strength exercise to improve daily tasks in older women: A randomized controlled trial. *Journal of American Geriatrics Society*, 53, 2–10.

22. Dowdy, D.B., Cureton, K.J., Duval, H.P., & Ouzts, H.G. (1985). Effects of aerobic dance on physical work capacity, cardiovascular function and body composition of middle-aged women. *Research Quarterly for Exercise and Sports*. 56(3), 227–233.

23. Dwyer, J. (1995). Effect of perceived choice of music on exercise intrinsic motivation. *Heath Values*, 19(2), 18–26.

24. Eickhoff-Shemek, J.M., & Selde, S. (2006). Evaluating group exercise leader performance. *ACSM Health & Fitness Journal*, 10(1), 20–23.

25. Eickhoff-Shemek, J.M., Herbert, D.L., & Connaughton, D.P. (2008). *Risk management for health/fitness professionals: Legal issues and strategies*. Baltimore, MD: Lippincott Williams & Wilkins.

26. Funk, D.C., Swank, A.M., Mikla, B.M., Fagan, T.A., & Farr, B.J. (2003). Impact on prior exercise on hamstring flexibility: A comparison of proprioceptive neuromuscular facilitation and static stretching. *Journal of Strength & Conditioning Research, 17,* 489–492.

27. Gotchalk, L., Berger, R., & Kraemer, W. (2004). Cardiovascular responses to a high-volume continuous circuit training protocol. *Journal of Strength & Conditioning Research, 18*(4), 760–764.

28. Grant, S., Davidson, W., Aitchison, T., & Wilson, J. (1998). A comparison of physiological responses and rating of perceive exertion between high-impact and low-impact aerobic dance sessions. *European Journal of Applied Physiology and Occupational Physiology, 78*(4), 324–332.

29. Grier, T.D., Lloyd, L.K., Walker, J.L., & Murray, T.D. (2001). Metabolic cost of aerobic dance bench stepping at varying cadence and bench heights. Abstract. *Medicine & Science in Sports & Exercise, 33*(5), S123.

30. Hamilton, N., Weimer, W., & Luttgens, K. (2008). *Kinesiology: Scientific basis of human motion* (11th ed.). Boston, MA: McGraw-Hill.

31. Herbert, D.L., & Herbert, W.G. (2002). *Legal aspects of preventive, rehabilitative, and recreational exercise programs* (4th ed.). Canton, OH: PRC Publishing.

32. Hoffman, S. (2009). *Introduction to kinesiology: Studying physical activity.* Champaign, IL: Human Kinetics.

33. Hostler, D., Schwirian, C.I., Hagerman, R.S., Staron, G., Campos, K., Toma, M.T., & Hagerman, G. (1999). Skeletal muscle adaptations in elastic resistance-trained young men and women. *Medicine & Science in Sports & Exercise, 31*(5), S1632.

34. Kravitz, L. (1994). The effects of music on exercise. *IDEA Today,* October, 55–63.

35. Kravitz, L., Greene, L., & Wongsathikun, J. (2000). The physiological responses to kickboxing exercise. Abstract. *Medicine & Science in Sports & Exercise, 35*(5), S148.

36. McCord, P., Nichols, J., & Patterson, P. (1989). The effect of low impact dance training on aerobic capacity, submaximal heart rate and body composition of college-aged females. *The Journal of Sports Medicine and Physical Fitness, 29*(2), 184–189.

37. McGill, S.M. (2007). *Low back disorders: Evidence-based prevention and rehabilitation* (2nd ed.). Champaign, IL: Human Kinetics.

38. McGinnis, P.M. (2005). *Biomechanics of sport and exercise.* Champaign, IL: Human Kinetics.

39. McMillan, D.J., Moore, J.H., Hatler, B.S., & Taylor, D.C. (2006). Dynamic vs. static-stretching warm up: The effect on power and agility performance. *Journal of Strength & Conditioning Research, 20,* 492–499.

40. Olson, M., Williford, H., Blessing, D., & Greathouse, R. (1991). The cardiovascular and metabolic effects of bench-stepping exercise in females. *Medicine & Science in Sports & Exercise, 23*(4), S27.

41. Requa, R.K., & Garrick, J.G. (1993). Injuries in various forms of aerobic dance. *Medicine & Science in Sports & Exercise, 25*(5), S270.

42. Ricard, M., & Veatch, S. (1990). Comparison of impact forces in high and low impact aerobic dance movements. *International Journal of Sports Biomechanics, 6*, 67–77.

43. Solomon, R.L., Solomon, J., & Cerny-Minton, S. (2005). *Preventing dance injuries.* Champaign, IL: Human Kinetics.

44. Thrash, L.E., & Anderson, J.J. (2000). The female athlete triad: nutrition, menstrual disturbances, and low bone mass. *Nutrition Today, 35*(5), 168–174.

45. U.S. Department of Health and Human Services. (2008). *2008 physical activity guidelines for Americans.* Washington, DC: Office of Disease Prevention and Health Promotion (U0036)/http://www.health.gov/paguidelines

46. Wilmore, J.H., Costill, D., & Kenney, W.L. (2008). *Physiology of sport and exercise* (4th ed.). Champaign, IL: Human Kinetics.

47. Wolfe, B.L., Lemura, L.M., & Cole, P.J. (2004). Quantitative analysis of single vs. multiple-set programs in resistance training. *Journal of Strength & Conditioning Research, 18*(1), 35–47.

SPECIAL POPULATIONS

Large-Sized Participant

1. American College of Sports Medicine. (2001). Position stand. Appropriate intervention strategies for weight loss and prevention of weight regain for adults. *Medicine & Science in Sports & Exercise, 33*, 2145–56.

2. American College of Sports Medicine. (2010). *ACSM's guidelines for exercise testing and prescription* (8th ed.). Baltimore, MD: Lippincott Williams & Wilkins.

3. American Dietetic Association. (2009). Position of the American dietetic association: Weight management. *Journal of the American Dietetic Association, 109*(2), 330–346.

4. Andersen, R., & Franckowiak, S. (1999). "Obesity." In ACE's *clinical exercise specialist manual.* San Diego, CA: American Council on Exercise.

5. Brownell, K.D. (1995). "Exercise in the treatment of obesity." In K.D. Brownell and C.G. Fairburn (Eds.), *Eating disorders and obesity: A comprehensive handbook* (pp. 473–478). New York, NY: The Guilford Press.

6. Ogden, C.L., Carroll, M.D., Curting, L.R., McDowell, M.A., Tabak, C.J., & Flegal, K.M. (2006). Prevalence of overweight and obesity in the United States, 1999-2004. *Journal of the American Medical Association*, 295, 1549–55.

7. U.S. Department of Agriculture & U.S. Department of Health and Human Services. (2005.). *Dietary guidelines for Americans*. Retrieved April 11, 2009, from www.healthierus.gov/dietaryguidelines

Prenatal Fitness

1. American Academy of Family Physicians. (2004). *Pregnancy: Things to think about before you're pregnant*. Retrieved June 29, 2009, from http://familydoctor.org/online/famdocen/home/women/pregnancy/basics/076.html

2. American College of Obstetricians and Gynecologists. (2003). *Exercise during pregnancy*. Retrieved April 26, 2010, from http://www.acog.org/publications/patient_education/bp119.cfm

3. American College of Sports Medicine. (2010). *ACSM's resource manual for guidelines for exercise testing and prescription* (8th ed.). Baltimore, MD: Lippincott Williams & Wilkins.

4. American College of Obstetricians and Gynecologists. (2002). Exercise during pregnancy and the postpartum period. Washington, D.C.: *ACOG Committee Opinion*, 99, 171–173.

5. American College of Obstetricians and Gynecologists. (2007). *You and your baby: Prenatal care*. Retrieved June 24, 2009, from http://www.acog.org/publications/patient_education/ab005.cfm

6. Aerobics and Fitness Association of America. (2008). *Perinatal Fitness*. Sherman Oaks, CA: Aerobics and Fitness Association of America.

7. Artal, R., Freeman, M., & McNitt-Gray, J. (1990). Orthopedic problems in pregnancy. *The Physician and Sports Medicine*, 18, 9.

8. Artal, R., Rutherford, S., Romen, Y., Kammula, R.K., Dorey, F.H., & Wiswell, R.A. (1986). Fetal heart rate responses to maternal exercise. *American Journal of Obstetrics and Gynecology*, 155.

9. Artal, R., & Subak-Sharpe, G.J. (1992). *Pregnancy and exercise*. New York, NY: Delacorte Press.

10. Artal, R., & Wiswell, R.A. (1986). *Exercise and pregnancy*. Los Angeles CA: Williams & Wilkins.

11. Center for Disease Control and Prevention. (2009). *Pregnancy planning education program*. Retrieved June 23, 2009, from http://www.cdc.gov/ ncbddd/pregnancy/

12. Clapp, J. (2008). *American Journal of Obstetrics and Gynecology*. Long term outcome after exercising throughout pregnancy: fitness and cardiovascular risk. 199(5). Mosby, Inc.

13. Hall, D.C., & Kaufman, D.A. (1987). Effects of aerobic and strength conditioning on pregnancy outcomes. *American Journal of Obstetric and Gynecology*, 157.

14. Lewis, B., Avery, M., Jennings, E., Sherwood, N., Martinson, B., & Crain, L. (2008). The effect of exercise during pregnancy on maternal outcomes: Practical implications for practice. *American Journal of Lifestyle Medicine.* Retrieved June 29, 2009, from http://www. medscape. com/viewarticle/580466

15. Medlineplus. (2008). *Should I exercise during my pregnancy.* Retrieved June 29, 2009, from http://www.nlm.nih.gov/medlineplus/magazine/ issues/winter08/articles/winter08pg26.html

16. U.S. Department of Health and Human Services. (2008). *Physical activity guidelines for Americans summary: Key guidelines for women during pregnancy and the postpartum period.* Retrieved June 29, 2009, from http://www.health.gov/paguidelines/guidelines/summary.aspx

Youth Fitness

1. American Academy of Pediatrics. (2001). Strength training for children and adolescents. *Pediatrics*, 107, 1470–1472.

2. American College of Sports Medicine. (2010). *ACSM's guidelines for exercise testing and prescription* (8th ed.). Baltimore, MD: Lippincott Williams & Wilkins.

3. Bar-Or, O. (1989). Trainability of the prepubescent child. *The Physician and Sportsmedicine*, 5, 64–82.

4. Centers for Disease Control and Prevention (2004). Nine million U.S. children diagnosed with asthma, new report finds. Retrieved on September 13, 2008 at http://www.cdc.gov/nchs/pressroom/04news/ childasthma.htm

5. Faigenbaum, A. D., Kraemer, W. J., Blimkie, C. J. R., Jeffreys, I., Micheli, L.J., Nitka, M. & Rowland, T.W. (2009). Youth resistance training: Updated position statement paper from the National Strength and Conditioning Association. Retrieved February 16, 2010 at http://www.nsca-lift.org/youthpositionpaper/Youth_Pos_Paper_ 200902.pdf

6. Kreamer, Williams J. and Fleck, Steven J. (1993). *Strength training for young athletes.* Champaign, IL, Human Kinetics Publishers, Inc.

7. National Association for Sports and Physical Exercise. (2004). *Physical activity for children: A statement of guidelines for children ages 5–12* (2nd ed.). Reston, VA: NASPE Publication.

8. Pangrazi, R.P., & Corbin, C.B. (1993). Physical fitness: Questions teachers ask. *Journal of Physical Education, Recreation and Dance*, 9, 14–19.

9. Pica, R. (1993). Responsibility and young children: What does physical education have to do with it? *Journal of Physical Education and Dance*, May/June: 72–75.

10. Roberts, S.O., & Weider, B. (1994). *Strength and weight training guide for young athletes.* Chicago, IL: Contemporary Books.

11. Rowland, T.W. (1990). *Exercise and children's health*. Champaign, IL Human Kinetics.
12. Sallis, J.F., et al. (1992). Determination of physical activity and interven tions in youth. *Medicine & Science in Sports & Exercise*, 24.6, S248–S257
13. Seefeldt, V. (1984). Physical fitness in preschool and elementary school aged children. *Journal of Physical Education, Recreation and Dance* November/December, 33–40.

Senior Fitness

1. Abbott, R.D., White, L.R., Ross, G.W., Masaki, K.H., Curb, J.D., & Petrovich, H. (2004). Walking and dementia in physically capable elderly men. *Journal of the American Medical Association*, 292, 1447 1453.
2. Administration onAging, U.S. Department of Health and Human Services. (2003). A statistical profile of olderAmericans aged 65+ *Snapshot*. Retrieved on November 16, 2005, from http://www.aoa.dhhs gov/press/fact/pdf/ss_stat_profile.pdf.
3. American College of Sports Medicine. (2000). Position stand: Exercise and type 2 diabetes. *Medicine & Science in Sports & Exercise*, 32, 1345 1360.
4. American College of Sports Medicine. (2002). *ACSM's resources fo clinical exercise physiology: Musculoskeletal, neuromuscular, neoplastic immunologic, and hematologic conditions*. Baltimore, MD: Lippincot Williams &Wilkins.
5. American College of Sports Medicine. (2009). *ACSM's exercise manage ment for persons with chronic diseases and disabilities* (2nd ed.) (J.L Durstine & G.E. Moore, Eds.). Champaign, IL: Human Kinetics.
6. American College of Sports Medicine. (2010). ACSM's guidelines fo exercise testing and prescription (8th ed.). Baltimore, MD: Lippincot Williams & Wilkins.
7. America College of Sports Medicine. (2010). *ACSM's reference manua for guidelines for exercise testing and prescription* (6th ed.). Baltimore MD: Lippincott Williams & Wilkins.
8. American Diabetes Association. (2003). Physical activity/exercise and diabetes mellitus: Position statement. *Diabetes Care*, 26 (Suppl.) S73-S77.
9. American Senior Fitness Association. (1995). *Senior fitness instructor personal trainer, and long-term care training manuals*. New Smyrna Beach, FL: American Senior Fitness Association.
10. American HeartAssociation. (2005). *Heart and stroke facts: 2005 statis tical supplement*. Dallas, TX:American HeartAssociation.
11. Barnes, P.J. (2000). Mechanisms in COPD: Differences from asthma *Chest, 117*(Suppl.), 10S-4S.
12. Best-Martini, E., & Botenhagen-DiGenova, K.A. (2003). *Exercise fo frail elders*. Champaign, IL: Human Kinetics.

13. Brandsma, J.W., Robeer, B.G., van den Heuvel, S., Smit, B.,Wittens, C.H., & Oostendorp, R.A. (1998). The effect of exercise on walking distance of patients with intermittent claudication: a study of randomized clinical trails. *Physical Therapy*, 78(3), 278-286.

14. Brill, P.A. (2004). *Functional fitness for older adults.* Champaign, IL: Human Kinetics

15. Clark, W.R. (2002). *A means to an end: The biological basis of aging and death*, New York, NY: Oxford University Press.

16. Clark, J. (2008). *Quality-of-life fitness* (2nd ed.). New Smyrna Beach, FL: American Senior Fitness Association.

17. Criqui, M.H. (2001). Peripheral arterial disease (epidemiological aspects). *Vascular Medicine*, 6, 3-7.

18. Estabrooks, P.A., & Carran, A.V. (2001). Predicting scheduling self-efficacy in older adult exercise: The role of task cohesion. *Journal of Aging and Physical Activity*, 8. 41-50.

19. Fagard, R. (2001). Exercise characteristics and the blood pressure response to dynamic physical training. *Medicine & Science in Sports & Exercise*, 33, S484-S492.

20. Fiatarone, M.A., O'Neill, E.F., Ryan, N.D., Clements, K.M., Solares, G.R., Nelson, M.E., et al. (1994). Exercise training and nutritional supplementation for physical frailty in very elderly people. *New England Journal of Medicine*, 330, 1769-1775.

21. Friedenreich, C.M. (2001). Physical activity and cancer prevention: From observational to intervention research. *Cancer Epidemiological Biomarkers Prevention*, 10, 287-301.

22. Guarente, L., & Kenyon, C. (2000). Genetic pathways that regulate aging in model organisms. *Nature*, 408(6809), 255-262.

23. International Council onActive Aging.(2005). *Motivation and reward systems that encourage activity*, Post Event Summary Report, as found at www. icaa.cc

24. Jones, C.J., & Rose, D.J. (2005). *Physical activity instruction of older adults.* Champaign, IL: Human Kinetics.

25. Liu-Ambrose, T., Khan, K., & McKay, H. (2001). The role of exercise in preventing and treating osteoporosis. *International Sports Medicine Journal*, 2(4), 1-13.

26. Rikli, R.E., & Jones, C.J. (2001). *Senior fitness test manual.* Champaign, IL: Human Kinetics.

27. Spirduso,W., Francis, K. & MacRae, P. (2005). *Physical dimensions of aging* (2nd ed). Champaign, IL: Human Kinetics.

28. Rose, D.J. (2003). *Fall proof! A comprehensive balance and mobility training program.* Champaign, IL: Human Kinetics.

29. Wolf, S.L. et al. (1996). Reducing frailty and falls in older persons: an investigation of tai chi and computerized balance training—Atlanta FICSIT Group: Frailty and Injuries—cooperative studies of intervention techniques. *Journal of American Geriatrics Society*, 44, 489–497.

30. U.S. Department of Health and Human Services. (2008). *2008 physical activity guidelines for Americans.* Washington, DC: Office of Disease Prevention and Health Promotion U0036)/www.health.gov/paguidelines.

MULTITRAINING®

Aqua Fitness

1. Becker, B. (2007). Healing waters. *Aquatics International*, 19(6),27–32.

2. Becker, B., & Cole, A. (Eds.). (1997). *Comprehensive aquatic therapy.* Newton, MA: Butterworth-Heinemann.

3. Chase, N.L., Sui, X., & Blair, S.N. (2008). Comparison of the health aspects of swimming with other types of physical activity and sedentary lifestyle habits. *International Journal of Aquatic Research and Education*, 2, 151–161.

4. D'Acquisto, L.J., D'Acquisto, D.M., & Renne, D. (2000). Metabolic and cardiovascular responses in older women during shallow-water exercise. *Journal of Strength and Conditioning Research*, 15(1),12–19.

5. DiPrampero, P.E. (1998). The energy cost of human locomotion on land and in water. *International Journal of Sports Medicine*, 7(2), 55–72.

6. Kennedy-Armbruster, C.A. (2009). Train the trainer. Presented at *ACSM Health & Fitness Summit*, March 27, 2009, Atlanta, GA.

7. Koury, J. (1996). *Aquatic therapy programming guidelines for orthopedic rehabilitation.* Champaign, IL: Human Kinetics.

8. McArdle, W., Katch, R., & Katch, V. (1991). *Exercise physiology, energy, nutrition and human performance* (3rd ed.). Pennsylvania, PA: Lea & Febiger.

9. Masumoto, K., & Mercer, J. (2008). Biomechanics of human locomotion in water: An electromyogrpahic analysis. *Exercise and Sport Sciences Reviews*, 36(3), 160–169.

10. Michaud, T., et al. (1995a). Comparative exercise responses of deep-water and treadmill running. *Journal of Strength and Conditioning*, 9(2), 104–109.

11. Michaud, T., et al. (1995b). Aqua running and gains in cardiorespiratory fitness. *Journal of Strength and Conditioning*, 9(2), 78–84.

12. Nagle, E.F., Robertson, R.J., Jakicic, J.J., Otto, A.D., Ranalli, J.R. & Chiapetta, L.B. (2007). Effects of aquatic exercise and walking in sedentary obese women undergoing a behavioral weight-loss intervention. *International Journal of Aquatic Research and Education*, 1, 43–56.

13. Peterson, J. (2006). 10 (Lame) reasons people commonly give for not exercising. ACSM's *Health & Fitness Journal*, 10(1), 44.

14. Quinn, T., Sedory, D., & Fisher, B. (1994). Physiological effects of deep water running following a land-based training program. *Research Quarterly for Exercise and Sport*, 65, 386–389.

15. Sanders, M. (Ed.). (2000). *YMCA, water fitness for health*. Champaign, IL: Human Kinetics. Retrieved June 26, 2007, from http://www.dswfitness.com

16. Sanders, M., & Maloney-Hills, C. (1998). Aquatic exercise for better living on land. *ACSM's Health & Fitness Journal*, 2(3), 16–23.

17. Sanders M.E., Constantino, N.E., Hsieh, J.J., & Rogers, M.E. (2007). Water-based exercise: Transfer of benefits to land for older women in the USA and Japan. *Medicine & Science in Sports & Exercise*, 39(5), Supplement, Abstract E-36.

18. Sanders, M.E. (2008). Splash! Cultivating a water exercise program for healthy activity using an evaluation approach. Part 1. *Journal on Active Aging*, 7(1), 56–64.

19. Takeshima N., Rogers, M.E., Wantanebe, E., Brechue, W.F., Okada, A., Yamada, T., Islam, M.M., & Hayano, J. (2003). Water-based exercise improves health-related aspects of fitness in older women. *Medicine & Science in Sports & Exercise*, 33(3), 544–551.

20. Whitehill, J., Constantino, N.L., & Sanders, M.E. (2008). *Cardiorespiratory and body composition responses to a water exercise program for athletes*. ACSM Southwest conference, November 20, 2008, Las Vegas, NV.

Low-Impact Aerobics

1. Aerobics and Fitness Association of America. (2010). Basic exercise standards and guidelines. In *Fitness: Theory & practice* (Laura A. Gladwin, Ed.). Sherman Oaks, CA: Aerobics and Fitness Association of America.

2. American College of Sports Medicine. (2010). *Guidelines for exercise testing and prescription* (8th ed.). Baltimore, MD: Lippincott Williams & Wilkins.

3. Bell, J., & Bassey, E. (1994). High- and low-impact aerobic dance heart rate and VO_2 responses. *European Journal of Applied Physiology*, 68, 20–24.

4. Kennedy-Armbruster, C., & Yoke, M.M. (2009). *Methods of group exercise instruction*. Champaign, IL: Human Kinetics. Champaign, IL: Human Kinetics.

5. Vertical Health. (2004). Low-impact aerobics. Retrieved on April 23, 2010 from http://www.diabetic-lifestyle.com/articles/mar04_burni_1.htm

Group Resistance Training

1. American College of Sports Medicine (2006). The recommended quantity and quality of exercise for developing and maintaining cardiorespiratory and muscular fitness and flexibility in healthy adults. *Medicine & Science in Sports & Exercise*, 30, 975–991.

2. American College of Sports Medicine. (2010). *Guidelines for exercise testing and prescription* (8th ed.). Baltimore, MD: Lippincott Williams & Wilkins.

3. Andersen, J.L., Schjerling, P., & Saltin, B. (2000). Muscle, genes and athletic performance. *Scientific American*, 9, 49.

4. Baechle, T., & Earle, T. (2003). *Essentials of strength training and conditioning* (3rd ed.). Champaign, IL: Human Kinetics.

5. Dorgo, S., King, G.A., & Rice, C.A. (2009). The effects of manual resistance training on improving muscular strength and endurance. *Journal of Strength & Conditioning Research*, 23(1), 293–303.

6. Hamilton, N, Weimer, W., & Luttgens, K. (2008). *Kinesiology: Scientific basis of human motion* (11th ed.). Boston, MA: McGraw-Hill.

7. McArdle, W.D., Katch, F.I., & Katch, V.L. (1996). *Exercise physiology: Energy, nutrition and human performance* (4th ed.). Baltimore, MD: Williams & Wilkins.

8. Pollock, M., Franklin, B., Baldy, G., et al. (2000). Resistance exercise in individuals with and without cardiovascular disease: Benefits, rationale, safety, and prescription. An advisory from the Committee on Exercise, Rehabilitation, and Prevention, Council on Clinical Cardiology, and American Heart Association. *Circulation*, 101, 828–833.

9. Staron, R.S., Leonardi, M.J., Karapondo, D.L., Malicky, E.S., Falkel, J.E., Hagerman, F.C., & Hikida, R.S. (1991). Strength and skeletal muscle adaptations in heavy-resistance-trained women after detraining and retraining. *Journal of Applied Physiology*, 70 (2), 631–640.

10. Thomas, M., Müller, T., & Busse, M.W. (2005). Quantification of tension in Thera-Band and Cando tubing at different strains and starting lengths. *Journal of Sports Medicine and Physical Fitness*, 45(2), 188–98, June.

11. Westcott, W.L. (1990). *Strength fitness: Physiological principles and training techniques* (3rd ed.). Dubuque, IA: William C. Brown.

12. Williams, M., Haskell, W., Ades, P., et al. (2007). Resistance exercise in individuals with and without cardiovascular disease: A scientific statement from the American Heart Association Council on Nutrition, Physical Activity, and Metabolism. *Circulation*, 116, 572–584.

13. Winnett, R.A., & Carpinelli, R.N. (2001). Potential health-related benefits of resistance training. *Preventive Medicine*, 33, 503–513.

14. Yoke, M. (2010). *Personal fitness training: Theory & practice* (Laura A. Gladwin, Ed.). Sherman Oaks, CA: Aerobics and Fitness Association of America.

Cardio Kickboxing

1. Aerobics and Fitness Association of America. (2010). *Kickboxing: A manual for instructors.* Sherman Oaks, CA: Aerobics and Fitness Association of America.
2. Boyer, J. (1999). *Boxing basics* course outline, AFAA authorized CEU program.
3. Dopps, B. (1999). Kickboxing explodes in health clubs. *ACE Certified News.* 5(2), 2–3.
4. Dyonn, C. (1999). *Triple threat* course outline, AFAA authorized CEU program.
5. Kravitz, L. (1999). Fight to be fit. *Ace Fitness Matters.* 5(1), 6–7.
6. Hamilton, N, Weimer, W., & Luttgens, K. (2008). *Kinesiology: Scientific basis of human motion* (11th ed.). Boston, MA: McGraw-Hill.

Step Training

1. American College of Obstetricians and Gynecologists. (2003). *Exercise during pregnancy.* Patient Education Pamphlet. Washington, DC: American College of Obstetricians and Gynecologists.
2. American College of Sports Medicine. (2010). *ACSM's guidelines for exercise testing and prescription* (8th ed.). Baltimore, MD: Lippincott Williams & Wilkins.
3. American Council on Exercise. (2001). Step Reebok guidelines. *Fit Facts.* MO1-076: 102.
4. Arthur C., Guyton, M.D., & Hall, J.E. (2000). *Textbook of medical physiology* (10th ed.). Philadelphia, PA: W.B. Saunders Co.
5. Caralco et al. (1991). The metabolic cost of six common movement patterns of bench step aerobic dance. *Medicine & Science in Sports & Exercise,* 23(4), Abstract #2140.
6. Clapp, J.F., & Little, K.D. (1994). The physiological response of instructors and participants to three aerobic regimens. *Medicine & Science in Sports & Exercise,* 26(8), 1041–1046.
7. Dawson, J., Juszczak, E., Thorogood, M., Foster, C., Marks, S.A., Dood, C., & Fitzpatrick, R. (2003). Distant past exercise in women: Measures may be reliable, but are they valid? *Medicine & Science in Sports & Exercise,* 35(5), 862–866.
8. Engels, H.J., Currie, J.S., Lueck, C.C., & Wirth, J.C. (2002). Bench-step training with and without extremity loading: Effects on muscular fitness, body composition profile, and psychological affect. *Journal of Sports Medicine and Physical Fitness,* 42(1), 71–78.
9. Francis, P. et al. (1994). *Introduction to step Reebok.* San Diego, CA: San Diego University.
10. Greenlaw, K. et al. (1995). The energy cost of traditional versus power bench step exercise at heights of 4, 6, and 8 inches. *Medicine & Science in Sports & Exercise,* 27(5), Abstract #1343.

11. Grier, T.D., Lloyd, L.K., Walker, J.L., & Murray, T.D. (2002). Metabolic cost of aerobic dance bench stepping at varying cadences and bench heights. *Journal of Strength and Conditioning Research, 16*(2), 242–249.

12. Kravitz, L. et al. (1995). Effects of step training with and without hand weights on physiological and lipid profiles of women. *Medicine & Science in Sports & Exercise, 27*(5), Abstract #1012.

13. Kravitz, L., Cisar, C.J., Christensen, C.L., & Setterlund, S.S. (1993). The physiological effects of step training with and without handweights. *Journal of Sports Medicine and Physical Fitness, 33*(4), 348–358.

14. Wang, M.Y., Flanagan, S., Song, J.E., Greendale, G.A., & Salem, G.J. (2003). Lower-extremity biomechanics during forward and lateral stepping activities in older adults. *Clinical Biomechanics, 18*(3), 214–221.

Mat Science®

1. Ansari, M., & Lark, L. (1998). Y*oga for beginners.* New York, NY: Harper Collins.

2. Calais-Germain, B. (1993). *Anatomy of movement.* Seattle, WA: Eastland Press.

3. Davis, C. (2009). *Contemporary theories in rehabilitation: Evidence for efficacy in therapy, prevention, and wellness.* Thorofare, NJ: Slack Incorporated.

4. Finger, A., & Bingham, A. (2000). *Introduction to yoga.* New York, NY: Three Rivers Press.

5. Friedman, P., & Eisen, G. (1980). *The Pilates method of physical and mental conditioning.* New York, NY: Doubleday & Co.

6. Gallagher, S.P., & Kryzanowska, R. (1999). *The Pilates method of body conditioning.* Philadelphia, PA: Trans-Atlantic Publications.

7. Hamilton, N, Weimer, W., & Luttgens, K. (2008). *Kinesiology: Scientific basis of human motion* (11th ed.). Boston, MA: McGraw-Hill.

8. McGinnis, P.M. (2005). *Biomechanics of sport and exercise.* Champaign, IL: Human Kinetics.

9. Robinson, L., & Thomson, G. (1998). *Body control: Using techniques by Joseph H. Pilates.* Philadelphia, PA: BainBridge Books.

10. Schiffman, E. (1996). *Yoga, the spirit and practice of moving into stillness.* New York, NY: First Pocket Books.

11. Windsor, M., & Laska, M. (1999). T*he Pilates powerhouse.* Cambridge, MA: Perseus Books.

12. Yogananda, P. (1993). *Autobiography of a yogi.* Self Realization Fellowship.